Blessed With Cancer

A Story of Courage, Love and Survival

Linda Mobley
Ronald Carr

This book is dedicated to:

Chanel…..my young, intelligent and beautiful daughter who was my reason for fighting and surviving through all the pain and suffering. Her constant encouragement, strength and personal courage at such a young age was my anchor and motivation. I love you.

and to:

My dad….a man full of wisdom and unconditional love, always my advocate no matter how big a mess. He believed in me and never gave up on me even when I didn't believe he could. He left this earth Thanksgiving Day, 2008.

"Blessings abound in this engaging memoir of a woman faced with the news we've all learned to fear and dread, that she has cancer, and how the resulting events reshape her world, her body and her spirit. Linda Mobley's encounter with cancer becomes an opportunity for her to connect with her loved ones and herself in ways she never could have anticipated, to discover hidden blessings in the most unexpected places, and to learn that sometimes we're strongest when we're most vulnerable."

Marilyn Clint
Associate Executive Director
Portland Rose Festival Foundation

"This inspiring, true-life story demonstrates the classic principle that we are not a victim of our circumstances, but a product of our choices. This journey of expanding awareness, taking personal accountability, and connecting with God's grace will inspire you to move to new heights."

Eric Allenbaugh, Ph.D., author of
Wake-Up Call: You Don't Have to Sleepwalk Through Your Life, Love or Career.
Deliberate Success: turning Purpose & Passion into Performance Results

Table of Contents

Foreword

Who, what, when, where, why and how?

It is the investigative maxim taught to us at an early age to prepare us for a life of hunting and gathering. A life spent searching for the truth and the facts – information pertinent to our belief (ultimately) in a purpose bigger than us. Journalists use "the five Ws and one H" to discern what their readers should know to have a complete picture of a story.

When a person is diagnosed with cancer "the five Ws and one H" flood every fiber of being – senses, processes, emotions, physical manifestations – everything. Like a tidal wave, a cancer diagnosis crashes into a sudden second of time and then filters through the canals of a person's life until every finite corner has been saturated.

Who am I...this person who now has cancer? What happened to bring me to this point? When did the cancer form and infiltrate my body? Where do I go from here? Why me, why now, why cancer? How do I do what I'm now supposed to do and how do I fight, live, survive, thrive...or, the unthinkable, die?

While it theoretically seeks the truth, this "five Ws and one H" instinct does not, in fact, lead to the discovery of the complete picture of cancer and a cancer diagnosis. It takes an "H" of a different maxim to fully envelope the truth and begin to understand cancer's purpose...it takes HOPE.

Proverbs 13:12 (NIV) says, "Hope deferred makes the heart sick, but a longing fulfilled is a tree of life." That longing to know the "story" behind a cancer diagnosis cannot be fulfilled with

Blessed with Cancer

facts or figures, or even having all the answers. It can be fulfilled through a willingness to step beyond who, what, when, where, why and how to faith, grace, mercy, love, hope and blessing (among so many others!) – the other investigative techniques God has equipped us with to uncover truth and discover purpose.

What makes "the five Ws and one H" so effective is their ability to draw more than yes or no from answers and inquiry. Such is the power and efficacy of God's information-gathering tools. Faith, grace, mercy, love, hope and blessing – as so heartwarmingly illustrated by Linda Mobley and Ronald Carr in Blessed with Cancer – can lead to the discovery of cancer's power to give life rather than take it away. Linda and Ron serve as journalists of a new kind in this powerful book as they approach Linda's yearning to understand cancer's purpose in her life with a bold, fresh and honorable approach.

As if conversing with a dear friend, Linda unveils her truths about cancer through stories and insights that are both endearing and encouraging. Her discovery reveals just how beautifully God's tools illuminate the truth beyond yes and no to the undeniable understanding that His plan is greater than cancer, greater than suffering, greater than scientific answers. Linda's honesty is wonderfully refreshing…she is a woman with needs, desires, talents, shortcomings and so many strengths, but she needed God's tools to move beyond the who, what, when, where, why and how tidal wave of her cancer diagnosis to the true BLESSING of cancer and its healing powers.

Linda's journey is a rich testimony to how much our Father God really does love His children. So much so that He will pursue us through our sometimes good and oftentimes bad choices and draw us closer to Him with miraculous, beautiful, at times horrific and always eye-opening revelations of His power and love. I believe this book serves to not only inspire cancer patients and survivors, but anyone who aspires to truly know and realize God's truth:

Blessed with Cancer

unfathomable grace and mercy, faithfulness, blessing, hope and love.

When reading Blessed with Cancer, allow your information-gathering instinct to blossom into a tree of life through hope – God's hope. As Romans 5:3-4 urges us, "...we also rejoice in our sufferings, because we know that suffering produces perseverance; perseverance, character; and character, hope."

Katie Harman Ebner
Miss America 2002

Introduction

Everyone knows how life is supposed to be, and in our minds we each know how we want it to be for us. A little baby girl is born to loving parents who themselves, have goals and dreams about this child and how her life is going to be. They are going to do everything within their power to make it perfect for her. First, she is loved and nurtured and constantly encouraged as she starts to crawl, then to walk and then to talk. It doesn't always happen in that order but in the first year or so of her life, that is how it goes. She is constantly in awe of life and continues to explore the world around her experiencing everything she can see, touch or feel. She even attempts to taste many things by putting them in her mouth. Sometimes that is a good experience, other times it is not. Most of the times her parents are always on the watch to make sure she is safe and that she experiences only the appropriate things like food, drink and an occasional treat.

As the early years go, her parents are also helping her to learn to read, write and prepare her to enter school as her education continues in a more formal way. She may go to pre-school or kindergarten as she begins her elementary school years and into middle school or junior high. Next, she experiences High School and that is a whole story in itself. Life-long friends are made and she finishes this level of her education and life experiences through her senior year. There is no other time in her life like her senior year, peppered with many fond, and some not so fond, experiences that she will carry throughout her life. Remember, this is how life is supposed to be.

After graduation, life seems to accelerate. She goes on to college to obtain a degree in the field that will help her achieve her life's goals and dreams, whatever they might be. She meets the perfect young man who sweeps her off her feet, and in time, they fall madly in love and get married. Eventually, they have children and new stories begin, which may be told in a different book. Every life on this planet and throughout the history of the world, even before the written word, has a story. Each is unique to the individual. Some are more exciting than others, intentionally or otherwise, but each follows a path that weaves a strand of history in the total fabric of mankind. But, again, that is another story for another time.

Now that she is married to the man of her dreams and they have a child of their own, their responsibilities increase as they nurture and help that child grow up into a wonderful person. And, when their child becomes a parent, they are then elevated to the prestigious life's role of grandparents. It is now an opportunity for them to love and nurture their grandchildren, fresh new young lives, from a new perspective and with different responsibilities. Their life experiences have provided them with maturity, insights, patience and profound wisdom, which they use to help mold these new and unblemished members of mankind.

Parents are responsible for raising, nurturing and disciplining children, which is not always easy and it is sometimes one of life's greatest challenges. On some occasions, the parents need to take a variety of disciplinary measures to help guide the child and keep them on the path to become successful human beings who are loving, caring, compassionate and successful members of society. Sometimes, it even does hurt the parents more than the child, although you could never convince the child of this point.

On the other hand, grandparents have the luxury of leaving the disciplining to the child's parents but being there only to console, empathize and understand when the child runs to them for comfort, understanding and reassurance. It is one of the greatest gifts of life, and not one of insignificance, to play this role. A grandparent gets to read books, tell stories, play games and

Blessed with Cancer

encourage along the way. They also have the chance to impart wisdom, direction and unconditional love to their grandchildren, maybe even through a perceived difficult time that the child is currently going through. That's their role, to be there for them, as a guide, a friend, a mentor or just someone that really cares for them, someone they can totally and completely trust. Grandparents are someone that loves them unconditionally, and gives them lots of hugs and kisses. During the tough times, they reassure the child that they are special, they are worthy, they are a good person, and that this experience will pass and life will be better. As a grandparent, this is one of life's greatest pleasures and a role that is so greatly needed in the world.

As life goes, and in a perfect world, we know there should be grandparents, maybe even great-grandparents, taking their part in raising children and grandchildren. Altogether, each of these individuals, together, makes up the family. And, in case we may have forgotten, the family unit is the foundation on which society stands. It is the foundation on which a nation should depend, and is the most critical element to the success and stability of that society. This, too, is another story for another time. When the grandparent is gone, this completes the circle of life. However, this is not the end; just the continuation of the circle as each person transitions to his or her new role in life. It's a good plan, and that's the way it should be.

Now that we know exactly how life is supposed to be, we realize that it is not always that way. Life provides challenges and obstacles, which we must learn to overcome, or to deal with in a way that we have a safe and successful outcome. It has been said that "what doesn't kill you, makes you stronger." I'm glad to say, that is true. However, while going through it, we sometimes wish it would kill us, so it would be over and we wouldn't have to feel the hurt, the pain, the rejection, the loneliness, the depression, feelings of hopelessness, sorrow and so many other emotions we experience. God does have a plan for our lives, although we don't always see

it, and sometimes we don't believe there is a God, let alone a God that even cares. I can tell you

there is and He does. I know, because He brought me through my experience, my nightmare,

where I lived out all my greatest fears.

You know how life is supposed to be and I thought I knew how it was supposed to be for me.

But that just wasn't so. I had no idea of what was yet to come or how my world would be turned

so upside-down. I'd never imagined that my life would be like an airplane spiraling out of

control, and that I was just waiting, or hoping for the crash, so it would all be over. Now, here's

how it really went.

*WHAT CANCER **CANNOT** DO.*

Cancer is so limited:

It cannot cripple love,

Shatter hope,

Corrode faith,

Destroy peace,

Kill friendships,

Suppress memories,

Silence courage,

Invade the soul,

Steal eternal life,

Or,

Conquer the spirit.

Author Unknown

Chapter 1 – The Discovery

"There is only one thing more painful than learning from experience, and that is not learning from experience." Archibald MacLeish

It was such a beautiful morning, the kind of morning that you would like to wake up to every day when absolutely everything is perfect. I'd slept extremely well and my body and mind were ready to get up, but I wanted to just lay there in bed a little longer and enjoy the quiet and peacefulness of a fresh new day. I'd slept so well during the night that I don't recall if I had dreamed at all. My bed was warm and comfortable and my blankets cradled me in their loving arms. The morning birds were just starting to sound their cheerful greetings back and forth to each other. The sounds of life and morning traffic were still non-existent at my level of awareness. The sun was just coming up so everything in the room was bathed in that wonderfully-warm, orange and peach glow. Not in a hurry to get up, I glanced around the room looking at the special lighting that God had given to the objects in the room. I was just taking everything in as if I was seeing some of it for the first time and the rest of it confirmed the safe and comfortable environment that I enjoyed in my own home. As my joy grew, all of this reminded me of a phrase I had heard so many times in my life, that "today is the day that the Lord hath made. I will rejoice and be glad in Him." Wow!! There is a God that cares for me and this morning confirmed it once again. However, there was more in store for me to discover yet today and I had no idea how my faith would be tested.

Morning is my favorite time of the day. I like to wake up early, pretty much before the rest of the world is up, and get my day started. Early morning is just different than the rest of the day, and for me, very special. For the most part, the weather doesn't really affect how I feel about the morning. If it's raining, that doesn't bother me. I love the way the world smells when Mother Nature is scrubbing it down. I can smell the freshness that rain brings, especially in the morning. If it is clear outside and I know it's going to be a warm, sunny day, it's exciting in a different way and for a different reason. Anticipation for the day is one of the really great gifts of the morning. I love to experience the dawning of each day just the way God presents it.

Sometimes in the morning, I would just lie in bed and watch the squirrels play outside my window. This is the northwest, and in my neighborhood, there were lots of squirrels. Sometimes I could hear them run across my roof, which is one of the experiences we all share up here. In the mornings, one squirrel in particular would circle down the trunk of this huge tree outside my window and, after reaching the bottom, would scurry back up and around again. It seemed to be a game, or maybe a courting ritual, with one squirrel chasing another. It was really cute and I enjoyed the entertainment.

Lying in bed for a few extra moments also gives me the opportunity to think about my day and what I'll be doing. I'll kind of list everything in my head and then ask myself what are the most important things I need to do today. I'd lay out a tentative mental plan about how I am going to get everything done, knowing full well that things may change and I need to be flexible. Sometimes, that's easier said than done. Have you ever heard the saying, "I don't know what I don't know?" Well, I just have to keep in mind that "things happen" and I need to deal with them as they do or just go with the flow. That thought alone relieves a lot of the pressure that comes with expecting everything to go just right. Life is too short to let things over which you have no control, affect you or take over your life. Starting the day with a mental plan gets you started in the right direction and helps you accomplish so much more. Once I'm up, showered,

Blessed with Cancer

dressed and ready to go, I write my plan down in my daily planner. It only takes a few minutes and I'm on my way. In all honesty, my day doesn't always go just this way. Remember, I said "things happen?" But, I do try to stay aware of this process and use it as much as possible. For the most part it works, and it's better than starting the day with no plan. I save the "no plans" approach for vacations and, on occasions, for weekends and holidays. But most of the time I like to head out the door with a plan of how I am going to get everything accomplished each day.

Today, like most of my days, is going to be busy. After taking Chanel to school, I will make my daily trip to the bank to go through the process of preparing my merchant's deposit from the business activities of the day before. My pet store business was doing well and I was blessed to be able to make decent deposits on a daily basis. Then, I will head over to the taxidermy to pick up a supply of custom-sized antler fragments. These make great chew bones for big and little dogs and are pretty popular items. It will take me 30 minutes to get over to the supplier and another 30 minutes back so I only make this trip once a week. The antlers sell surprisingly well so I'll make sure I have a good supply for the upcoming weekend. My next stop will be at the Dollar Store to pick up a supply of bags and baggies of various sizes. I'll use these for placing the items my customers purchase so they'll have something with which to carry them home. I'll also pick up a weekend supply of other odds and ends such as little trinkets, balls, miniature animals or any other little item that fits the theme of my store or adds an element of fun for my customers. Much of this is for the "impulse" shopping that many customers like to do and, in some cases, expect to do. None of these items are expensive, but I'm able to make a good return on the product investments.

Next, I'll need to get to the store and make sure it is open and ready for business. I am training a high school girl who comes in after school so I'll need to be ready to do that. She's learning to help out and will eventually run the store when I'm not there. I need to make sure everything else is taken care of so I have time to train her. Thursday is also the day when I place my weekly orders for new products and for restocking the supplies of pet food. I've got the routine down so it won't take a lot of time. It's important, though, and needs to get done.

As if I'm not busy already, sometime this afternoon I am going to have find time to get my hair and nails done. This is not normally one of my Thursday routines but I was asked to attend a Making Memories Foundation "Tea and Fashion Show" tomorrow and will be attending on behalf of my good friend Annette. Annette passed away from cancer a few months ago, and I have the opportunity to share her story with the audience. During the tea, there will be a fashion show fundraiser for Making Memories. Beautiful ladies will model donated wedding dresses which will be offered for say to the audience. The proceeds will go to help support the Making Memories organization. I'm looking forward to it. I wanted to do something more to help so I volunteered my store as the designated drop-off place for the wedding dresses that will be modeled during the show. Over the past week people have been coming to my store with the donated dresses and I expect a few more today. Later this afternoon, Making Memories will pick up all the dresses and prepare them for the fashion show.

Now it was *my* time to get into the shower and start preparing myself for the day. As I stepped under the warm water, I was thinking about how really perfect my life was. I had just started a new business, Chanel and I had recently moved into a new condominium and we were rebuilding our lives. With the loss of a friend recently and all that Chanel and I had gone through, I had a real hunger in my soul to grow spiritually and was excited with anticipation for what God had in store for us next.

Blessed with Cancer

For me the shower is always a pleasant morning ritual as I wash off whatever remaining sleep has hold of me. The warm water jump-starts my circulation as my physical body prepares itself for the demands of the day. As a business woman and mother, with responsibilities for my customers and my daughter, I always feel I am better prepared when my body and mind are warmed up. Standing under the warm water and feeling it cascading down my body, I use this time to stretch my neck, shoulders and arms. Then I do some twisting exercises for my torso, stretching my stomach and back muscles as I go. These are not full-blown gym exercises but more like gentle motion movements to get out the kinks and stretch the muscles. You probably have a routine of your own that helps get you started in the morning. That's great.

I really do enjoy starting my day this way because, while I am preparing physically, I also find this routine to be very relaxing and it helps me to also prepare mentally. In one sense, it helps me get my head on straight, my attitude right and my enthusiasm for life all in their right places. I feel it makes all the difference in the world on how my day will go. You see, I love what I do which, for the most part, is relating to people and raising my daughter, Chanel. Sure, I have a store that provides products and services but to me, what I do is all about relationships with my family, friends and customers. I enjoy life and want to have fun with it and I want to be a catalyst to help other people enjoy their lives too. I've already had enough heartaches and tragedies in my life to write another book but I don't want that to be my focus. Some people are so caught up in the past and what hasn't gone right for them that they just can't see what opportunities lay before them. That's not me! I've made my mistakes, taken my lumps and I've learned to move on. I want to experience all the best there is about life and the people we come in contact with everyday. As you can tell, I'm feeling very good this morning.

5

Blessed with Cancer

Before I got into the shower I had already awakened Chanel and she was getting herself ready for school. She is only ten years old but already very responsible and mature for her age. She is the love of my life and so much fun to have around. Although I am her mother and she is my only child, we have a great relationship and we are more like very good friends. Only occasionally do I need to exert myself in the "adult-child" relationship scenario that I was taught back in psychology class. Chanel and I do everything together and share so much. Because of my physical size, five feet one inch in height and one hundred and one pounds soaking wet, we are about the same size. This means that when we play together, especially physical games, we are pretty equally matched. Thank goodness I have the advantage of experience, maturity and wisdom. I'm glad I have that because I think in a few years I will be looking up to her. Chanel is a delight and I couldn't love her more. I'm also pretty confident she would say the same about me. What I didn't know back then was how much I was going to need her love and her strength in such an important way. I also didn't realize how grown-up she would need to be and how our roles would reverse. We were both going to learn new things.

I must have really been enjoying my shower and was caught up in thinking about the day. I wasn't daydreaming but was so relaxed in the moment I didn't hear Chanel call to me. Finally, my "mom" radar started to pick up the sound of her calls. Faintly at first, I heard "mom" but it still hadn't fully registered. Then, again, but stronger, I heard "Mom", then "MOM!" My motherly instincts finally kicked in, I snapped to total awareness and I realized something must be wrong. Why else would Chanel be calling me in such a frantic way?

Since I was still in the shower, and quite wet, I turned off the water and quickly grabbed my towel. When someone is calling for you and you think it may be urgent it seems like whatever

Blessed with Cancer

you are doing takes so much longer than it normally would. I'm really not a very big person, so I should have been able to dry off in seconds but at the time it felt like it was taking forever.

I was just about done and was rubbing the towel across my chest one more time when I felt something I had never noticed before. It stopped me cold. I had a sudden realization that I didn't want to have. Still in disbelief, I wiped the towel across the spot a couple more times to see if "the lump" I felt was really there, and it was. Could it be and why was it happening now? I wasn't ready to accept the spot for what the growing fear in my stomach was telling me. At that moment, everything else around me was forgotten. Now all of my focus was on a spot just above my left breast. I'd even forgotten that just a moment ago Chanel had been calling for me about some urgent matter.

I switched the towel to my left hand so I could better use the fingers of my right to study the spot further to confirm if there was really something there. There was something and it was there and there was no denying its existence. Believe me, I tried. There was a lump and it was obvious enough that my fingers could feel it very well. It was the size and shape of a small lima bean. I struggled to get a sense of its texture, which was more difficult, but I could feel it was solid enough that it wouldn't break apart or dissolve as I pushed at it or tried to squeeze it. As I stood there feeling the lump I started giving myself a complete breast exam, just as I had learned to do over the years. I began checking all over both breasts to see if there were any other spots or lumps that I had also not detected before. I couldn't find any and kept coming back to the one lump that so cruelly interrupted and took over my perfect morning.

After checking the spot about six times, trying not to think about this, my worst fear, it finally hit me in the stomach like a dull thud. I felt as if someone had sneaked up on me when I was least prepared and punched me as hard as they could in my gut. All my worst fears about cancer

7

Blessed with Cancer

came rushing in from all directions and collided in one huge explosion in the pit of my stomach. I couldn't breath and my legs struggled to hold me upright. I was instantly so sick I thought I was going to throw up. I remember thinking, "Oh, my God, what is happening!"

To this day, I don't know if I really just thought "Oh my God," or if I actually uttered those words out loud, over and over again while making my way into my bedroom. At that moment my bedroom seemed so far away. I was moving as if I was caught in a state of slow motion. I just couldn't get there fast enough. I was so overcome and weak I needed to make it to my bed and lay down before I collapsed. I couldn't hold back the tears, as I settled on my bed. All the stress of this realization was pouring out of my eyes. I wasn't bawling like I thought I might. My tears just flowed uncontrollably. Perhaps I was too focused on sorting out my thoughts, but nothing would audibly come out of my mouth. My mind was racing to find answers, the kind that would re-assure me it wasn't true and that I was just overreacting.

Lying on my back I continued my breast exam, almost in automatic mode. I was overcome with emotion. I stared toward the ceiling, trying to look past my earthly surroundings and into Heaven for answers. Is it really cancer or something else? It's got to be something else! This can't be happening to me. There has to be a logical explanation for this instant lump in my breast. If it were really cancer and as large as it is, wouldn't I have noticed it sooner? I had just recently lost a good friend to cancer and didn't want to believe it was really happening to me. No! It isn't!! It's not happening! After another deep breath, I tried to calm down and will it away. It's probably just a pimple, or a boil, or some other naturally occurring irritation under my skin. It didn't work. Nothing was working. All this time, while looking for a way out of this realization with some rational explanation and denying the reality now facing me, I knew deep down in my heart and soul it was cancer. Cancer! Damn that word!

Blessed with Cancer

I don't know how I knew it was cancer but I did. Lord knows, I didn't want to believe it and I tried to get away from it but there was just no way out. Even my constant praying was not going to change that. Prayer is powerful and, as a believer, I know God has a plan for my life. However, I couldn't believe or accept that this was part of that plan. I didn't want to believe it. I know that there is a season and a reason for everything but this just isn't the way my life is supposed to be going. Up until about twenty minutes earlier my life was going just fine. In spite of my faith and all I was taught to believe in and trust in, I kept asking, "God, why me……and why now?

Chapter 2 – Taking the Steps

*"What you are afraid to do is a clear indicator of
the next thing you need to do."*   Robert Anthony

"Mom… MOM!! What's wrong?" Chanel finally got my attention and broke me out of my self-absorbed drama. *"Nothing, honey, I'm just thinking."* I couldn't tell her what was really going on. I didn't want to believe it myself. I was still in shock and in a semi-state of denial. All my fears were telling me it is cancer and if it is, I can't let Chanel know. She mustn't know. No, she can't know. Having lost our friend Annette just a few short months ago, I can only imagine what it would do to her and how she would react. Chanel saw Annette's struggle and her eventual death and I was afraid of how she would react. After all, she is only 10 years old. She may have been able to handle the news but I wasn't really sure. Maybe I didn't give her the credit for the incredible and strong young lady she's turned out to be. Still, I chose to pull myself together and pretend this was just another day. I would distract her and get us both back on the task of getting ready for school and work.

I sat up. *"Chanel, you were calling for me. What did you need? You sounded rather frantic."* Maybe this hasn't happened to you but I felt a little bit guilty, especially when I think I'd been caught. You know, like when someone is talking to you and you're not really paying attention. It's embarrassing to be asked a question and not know how to answer because I wasn't listening. It wasn't that I didn't hear her…it was because I wasn't paying attention to her. I focused and gave that attentive look, and tried to act concerned, although I was really feeling like I was a step behind. If I answer wrong, I'll expose myself and she will know I wasn't paying attention. I should have been listening, because when she was calling earlier, before my attention was

Blessed with Cancer

diverted, she sounded like something was very wrong. It could have been something really serious and because I didn't react, I don't know what might have happened.

"So, Chanel, what did you need? With a frantic look of desperation on her face, she said "I can't find my pink socks with the elephants on them." *"Oh my gosh!"* I couldn't believe it. This was the critically urgent matter that prompted my wonderful, intelligent and resourceful daughter to run through the house out of control and in a state of panic, calling for her mom? I was stunned, and to think she wasn't even a teenager yet. You'd have thought she only owned one pair of socks. I know for a fact that she has a drawer full of socks of various colors and patterns. However, the missing pink socks were her favorite.

I didn't know what to say, or how to react. I wasn't sure if I should be irritated and really get after her or if I should start laughing hysterically out loud. It was so ridiculous. At least to this adult, it was funny. However, to a ten year old girl who was planning the perfect outfit to wear to school, it was probably a lot more urgent. Thinking back, though, I believe it was just the outrageously perfect distraction to get my mind off myself and back into life as it should be. I wasn't oblivious to the fact that I had just discovered a lump that needed to be investigated, but I was now mentally back to dealing with what I needed to do to get through the day.

The day went pretty much the way every Thursday went, starting with getting Chanel up, fed and delivered safely to school. Still, I was pre-occupied all throughout the day because of the burden I was now carrying. I had discovered a lump. I believe it is cancer, but don't really know, and I don't want it to be. I was trying to be logical and figure it all out but just didn't want to accept what it might be. I felt the lump over and over again throughout the day to see if it was really there, as if by rubbing it, it would miraculously go away. I still had to get my work done, run my business and make sure I was ready for the weekend.

Blessed with Cancer

At one point during the day, I had to stop and call my friend Fran Hansen with the Making Memories Breast Cancer Foundation. I needed to finalize my participation in tomorrow's Fundraising Tea. I couldn't decide if I should tell her about my discovery over the phone, because I really didn't know for sure, or if I should wait and tell her in person at the Tea. It was difficult to hold back. I wanted someone with whom to share my burden. I know there was nothing she could do but I just needed to tell someone. Fran's a good listener and would know how to settle me down and comfort me. She is also a good friend and would tell me not to panic or assume the worst until I had a chance to speak to the doctor. She would also have told me to see the doctor immediately and not wait.

I couldn't help myself. I told her. *"Fran.......I found a lump."* First there was silence, probably only a couple of seconds but it seemed like a long time to me. I wanted to hear Fran tell me that it couldn't possibly be true. On her end, I think she was trying to comprehend if she heard me right. When she finally spoke, she said "What!? What did you say?" I repeated that I had found a lump and briefly shared my story of the morning. As I hoped, Fran understood very quickly and began re-assuring me that things would be okay, that it probably wasn't cancer but if it was, things were going to be okay. With understanding and encouragement, she gave me the re-assurance that I needed. She also, in her warm and motherly way, made me agree that I would call the doctor as soon as possible and get in to see him. Perhaps this was a good thing. If it was cancer, I had found it early. As Fran knows, there are too many women that refuse to accept the possibility and don't have themselves checked as they should. Fran knows that with early detection, the chances of a woman's survival are considerably increased. She is a good friend and said all the right things. She also assured me that she would be there to help in any way possible.

Blessed with Cancer

I deliberately tried to keep busy and stay focused on my business. Thank goodness my day was full and for the most part already scheduled. I was running from one work activity to the next, just as I did everyday, without incident. However, whenever I had a spare moment, the pending doom of what I had just discovered would explode to the front of my head and I would start thinking about "the lump." Not knowing anymore than I knew first thing this morning, my consciousness would become consumed with the fear that had taken over earlier in the day. I hated it. I didn't want to think about it. Call it denial. I suppose, in some way, I was in denial but at the time I really didn't think I had gotten to that stage. I think it was more a case of "avoidance" of even acknowledging that something was going on. If it is cancer, I'm going to die. If it isn't there, then it isn't cancer, and my life will go on as it has for years. Even if it is there, it couldn't be cancer. How could it possibly be cancer?

I had just spent the last year and a half with my friend, trying to make life better for her. I always believed that she would beat it, yet was fearful she wouldn't. I'm pretty certain it is not contagious. What do you think are the odds that I could come down with cancer right after the loss of my friend? If there are odds, I would think they are pretty astronomical in my favor that it's not cancer. Therefore, whatever I have in my breast that has raised this fear in me couldn't be cancer. I mean really, it couldn't possibly be cancer. *"Keep telling yourself, Linda,"* my mind would say. *"There has to be a logical explanation."* I tried to rationalize why this couldn't be happening to me. *"I'm too healthy....so much in my life is starting to go right. God wouldn't let this happen to me, and not now."* It made me feel so much better after I reasoned why it wasn't possible for me to have cancer, and why it couldn't happen to me. If I didn't know better, someone might be able to convince me that I may have been in denial. *"Me? What's to deny? After all, if I did have it, wouldn't I know? And, if I didn't have it, shouldn't I also know? If I do*

Blessed with Cancer

have it, they'll tell me and then we'll devise a plan to fix it. If I don't have it, then I will wonder

why I was so caught up in all the fuss. Why am I spending so much time thinking about it"? It's

like being caught in a dream and trying to resolve the dream, even though you know it is not real.

Regardless, you continue to try fixing it, all the while knowing you can't. You have no control.

So stop beating yourself up. That is the discussion I would have with myself all weekend, which

seemed a lifetime. Finally, exhausted, I had to let it go. I decided that I didn't have cancer, so

there! *"Thank God,"* I told myself, *"that's settled. Now I can get back to my life."* That's just

one more argument in my head, with myself, but I'm not sure if I won or not. Wow! All that

effort and nothing was really settled at all.

I should have been exhausted when I went to bed Thursday night, which I was, and should

have slept through the night, but I didn't. It was one of those rough nights and seemed to go on

forever. I tossed and turned, feeling like I never did fall asleep. I tried to keep my eyes closed

but, suddenly, I'd open them and the minute hand on the clock just wasn't moving. My mind

would not quit. Against hope, I couldn't stop thinking about the possibility that I did have

cancer. I tried to rationalize it away. In essence, I was trying to resolve this nightmare but I

wasn't dreaming, and there was nothing I could do but pray and beg God to take this away.

"Please God, don't let this be real. You have a plan for my life. Surely, this isn't it?"

I got up Friday morning and prepared myself to fulfill the commitment I'd made to support

the Making Memories foundation, as promised. I was supposed to be there to speak on behalf of

my friend Annette. I joined in the tea party with Making Memories, numb from the sleepless

night and the constant worry. It was kind of weird being invited to be there on behalf of Annette,

while at the same time knowing I have a newly discovered lump in my own breast. *"What am I*

Blessed with Cancer

doing here? How can I share Annette's story without it becoming my story. Oh, God. Please help me get it together."

At times, the anxiety was smothering but I had to go on with the program. I'd made a commitment and people were counting on me. I spoke about my friend and tried to share how hard she'd fought, how much she wanted to survive. But, at one point, Annette must have realized it wasn't to be. She became calm and did what she could to make her remaining time memorable for her sons. It was so hard to tell her story without choking up a number of times. I must admit, it was a tear jerker. I only hope that I gave honor to Annette and her life, while saying something that would encourage others never to quit the fight. I believe God has a plan for each of us. I know He is still working with me, but I hope His plan for Annette's life was fulfilled. Maybe I will understand that some day.

All weekend was like a seesaw for me and I had no control over the up and down of emotions. I was up and down......up then down, and in a constant state of experiencing fear and then relief. The conversations I had with myself over the rest of the weekend were ongoing. As much as I tried to keep myself distracted, it wasn't working. So far, I think this was the longest weekend of my life and it wasn't over yet. *"Would Monday ever get here?"*

Monday finally came. In one way, I was relieved. As it was throughout the weekend, this was just the beginning of many sleepless nights and pre-occupied days. Whatever the outcome I knew I would have to do whatever it takes if I was going to survive this. I couldn't just give in to my fear. I had to tell myself again that if there is a cancer monster, I will have to beat it before it kills me. A number of people said it was like I was in a state of shock. Perhaps I was. I had just gone through the death of Annette, a divorce, while still trying to run a business and be a single mom. I suppose I was in shock but I just had to push through it. Maybe you know exactly

Blessed with Cancer

what I am talking about or maybe you can only imagine! It seemed overwhelming and, at times, impossible. My only consolation was that I knew in my heart that God had a plan for my life. I hoped I would survive so He would have time to show me. Here I am again, questioning God's timing. In the midst of it all, I sometimes forgot that God does everything on time. He is never early and He is never late. His purposes happen at just the right time.....and on time.

It was Monday morning and was actually a beautiful, sunny day. That is a good sign, at least for me. I checked for my lump again and, yes, it was still there. I took a shower to wash away the night and prepare myself for the visit to the doctor. I was thinking what it must have been like for Annette when she found her lump. Did she ask all the questions I am asking? How did she handle it? All I knew at that moment was that she is gone.

After breakfast, I got Chanel off to school and headed to my doctor appointment. But, before I could do that, I had to call a friend and make arrangements for Chanel to be picked up when school let out. I was still responsible for my pet food store and also had to make sure that my customers were taken care of. My dad agreed to come down and cover the store until I could get there. I was single and alone, so I had to work all these things out. Wouldn't it be nice if some things just took care of themselves?

A female friend of mine gave me a ride to the doctor's office. When I'd made the appointment, the scheduling nurse recommended that I get someone to drive me in case I needed a ride home. She said it may be necessary if the doctor decided to biopsy the lump. I also think it helped me face the day by having this kind of support from a caring friend. I wasn't doing it all alone. When I told a few people about the lump, and that it might be cancer, it seemed like they tried to be encouraging but mostly what I sensed was doom and gloom. That wasn't helpful. I just wanted to get to the doctor's office and have it checked out. I was trying to make

Blessed with Cancer

light of it all so that everyone wouldn't be so serious. At the moment, I needed to feel hope, not despair. I needed encouragement, not fear or loss. I needed to know that someone understood and was going to help me.

I was a little surprised when I arrived at the doctor's office and found that the medical staff was matter-of-fact about the whole thing. I expected more concern but they were pretty nonchalant about my condition. From the moment I arrived, they just went about their jobs like there was nothing different about today. I'm thinking: *"Don't they realize how serious this is? Don't they know that my lump might mean I have cancer? It might even be life-threatening."* I thought that everyone at the doctor's office should take my visit a little more serious and treat me like I am special. After all, aren't I? It started to concern me because I thought everyone should be a lot more professional in this place. In reality, they were all professional.

Although the tumor wasn't visible to the naked eye, when I ran my hand across my chest I could feel something under the skin. And, when I pressed on it, it pushed in. This tumor had its own consistency, and felt to me a lot like a soft Nerf ball. I was told that most cancer lumps are small and hard, much like a bee-bee. But mine was different.

They finally called my name and led me into one of the examining rooms. I changed from my clothes and put on the glamorizing gown. You know...the kind where you have to decide what part of your anatomy would most likely be exposed. I didn't know at the time that it would soon be a style to which I would become accustomed. So much for my modeling career. I climbed onto the examining table, trying not to show the anxiousness on my face in front or the full-moon smile in back. Then they began a process of taking measurements. They seemed to measure everything....my chest, my waist, the area around the lump, the distance between different points on my chest in relation to my shoulders, breasts, nipples, belly button and breast bone. *"Are they really going to need all those?"* I couldn't really see what they were doing. I could only feel the activity as they were busy probing and prodding.

The next step was to do an ultra-sound. As I lay on the table, they applied the gel and started moving the instrument around to get the best angles possible to determine what they were seeing. Although this procedure went very quickly, I was a little anxious. No one was talking or telling me what they were seeing. I was trying to watch their faces to see if I could read their reactions. They were strictly professional and well guarded in their facial expressions. My anxiety grew as I thought I was only seeing concern on their faces. *"This is terrible"*, I thought. *"Somebody please say something. Talk to me, would you?"*

I guess the doctor felt he had enough evidence for real concern and made the decision that the tumor needed to come out. There was enough difference in how the lump felt that he needed to be able to have it studied directly and run through a series of tests; I was prepped for the removal procedure.

It all happened so suddenly I was a little stunned, maybe even shocked. I didn't think we would do this right now. I guess I didn't realize that they would take this step today and do a procedure so quickly. It must have been more urgent than I'd thought. I was hoping they would say it wasn't anything serious, or at least send me home to come back a few days or a week later. At least that way, I would have been more prepared. I wasn't ready and hadn't prepared myself mentally for this sudden step. I came in confident that everything would be all right and, if not, I was ready to do whatever, but the sudden panic caught me by surprise. They went about the business of readying themselves for a procedure they have probably done thousands of times. Apparently, they had everything they needed at the clinic, including the capable staff to do the procedure right here and right now. Once again, I had to take another deep breath and just hold

Blessed with Cancer

on for the ride. I had no control. *"Lord, please guide the doctor and nurses as they do what they need to do to help me. I place my trust in You to guide their hands. Amen."*

I thought this would be a simple procedure but the lump was deep enough that they needed to anesthetize me. Numbing the area wasn't going to do it. They needed to do more. I climbed into the bed and the nurse hooked me up with an IV. I appreciated the fact that the IV they inserted in the top of my hand made it possible to only be stuck once and then everything else is administered through the IV. I like that. Finally, something "magical" was shot into my IV and, almost immediately, I went to sleep.

The next thing I knew, I could faintly hear a distant voice saying, "Linda, can you hear me? It's all over and you're going to be waking up soon. Can you move your hand?" I could hear them and I tried to move my hand. At first, I wasn't sure anything was happening but they kept talking to me, repeating the instructions. There seemed to be a disconnect but I was trying. It may have only been for a short time but it seemed like it was taking me way too long to respond. Finally, the nurse said, "That's good. Keep doing that." I must have moved my hand or maybe it was just my fingers. I still wasn't sure, but I think I was coming back.

When I finally left the doctor's office I had a sense of relief. I thought the doctor had given me a reason, a ray of hope, to believe that it wasn't cancer. He didn't say that specifically but that was my interpretation. That's what I wanted to believe. What he did say was that after examining the lump, it didn't look black and gritty like most cancers so he felt good about that. That was my ray of hope. However, when they removed the mass of tissue my little lima bean-shaped tumor had small tentacles coming out of it, reaching for other parts of my body. This concerned the doctor and I sensed it was more than just concern. He tried to downplay it but I

20

Blessed with Cancer

wasn't buying it. After all, he was an expert in this field and I suspect he has seen all kinds. In fact, he has probably seen it all.

I had only been in the clinic for a few hours when I was finished and it was time for me to go home. My friend had stayed there for me, and was waiting to drive me home. Although I was weak and needed to go home, I still wanted to drop by my store and see how things were going. I was relieved and grateful when it was clear that my dad had it all under control. There was nothing for me to be concerned about at all. Dad came through.

I was really starting to feel better so, instead of heading home for some rest, I decided to hang out at the store for a while and visit with my daughter and some of our customers. They had heard about the procedure and everyone wanted to know how I was doing. I don't remember much of the details or everything I said and I am sure some of it didn't make sense. It was probably a combination of still having the anesthesia in my system, as well as the benefits of some strong medication for the minor procedure that had taken place. In fact, I was feeling no pain. Life was good and I was just enjoying the ride.

The afternoon passed quickly and I was enjoying myself so much I stayed until it was time to close the store. Then dad took me and Chanel out to dinner. I don't know why but I was famished for Asian food, so we went to my favorite Chinese restaurant. It felt so good to be alive and to be spending the evening with my daughter and her grandfather, my dad. What a great place to be. I was reminded again that having a family is such a blessing and, too often, we forget how important they are. I was just taking it all in.

Later that evening when I finally crawled into bed, it was so easy for me to snuggle up in my warm sheets and blanket and nod off to sleep. But before I did, I needed to take a few moments to pray that everything would be alright. The procedure today was only the beginning and there

Blessed with Cancer

were still too many unanswered questions. The lump was still on my mind. As I prayed, I asked God for it not to be cancer. *"Please God, there's got to be some other explanation. It can't be cancer. It just can't be cancer."*

For me, falling asleep that night was a blessing. I was so tired at that moment that I slept through the night, not even thinking about the next two weeks that would seem to become the longest of my life. The procedure was over, the tumor had been removed and now I would have to wait for two weeks until the results of the biopsy came back from the lab. I don't know why they can't just find out now and let me know. Why does it have to take two weeks? What am I supposed to do in the meantime? It would be the "not knowing" that was so hard to live with. But, for now, I was too numb and too tired to think about these questions, so falling into a deep sleep, at least for tonight, was a blessing. I'll face it all tomorrow.

Chapter 3 – B-Day V-Day

*"When I thought I couldn't go on, I forced myself to keep going...
My success is based on persistence, not luck."*   Estee Lauder

The decision was made. They are going to have to remove both of my breasts. I did everything I could and followed my doctor's instructions to the letter but the outcome I'd hoped for was not to be. Together, we decided the next step. There were no other options.

It seemed like only a few weeks ago when I first discovered the lump in my left breast. I'd found it early and took steps immediately to deal with the horrific discovery. I got to my doctor right away. He confirmed the lump was cancer and referred me to the specialist, the oncologist that would take over my case and do what he could to help me. After the examination, as we discussed the options, he told me he was going to do everything in his power to help me keep my breasts. He felt that if he could remove the lump, the infected areas around where the lump had been, and take as little as possible he may be able to minimize the damage.

I loved the fact that he was so "up front" with me and told me everything. He described, as much as possible in layman terms, what he would need to do and how he would approach the surgeries. He was very skilled and came highly recommended, and my primary doctor had told me he was the best around. Whether he was or not I have no way of knowing, but I believed he was the best. I had to have that belief. It was important for me to have complete faith in the man I was entrusting with not just my breasts, but my life as well. I believe it's important, or even critical, in such a relationship. I asked lots of questions and he patiently took the time to answer me and explain what he was going to do next. He also shared with me the anticipated outcome of each procedure and was constantly encouraging me. He had been through this so many times before with other patients and seemed to instinctively understand my needs and fears. He also went to great lengths to put me at ease and I was so grateful for the personalized attention. This wonderful and gifted man was such a committed professional. His assuring bed-side-manner gave me the hope I needed to get through this. I knew in my heart he would take care of me.

The plan for the first surgery was to just remove the necessary muscle and other tissues that were likely to be infected with the disease. Based on blood and tissue samples, they could determine the approximate degree to which the cancer was spreading but they wouldn't really know for sure until after each surgery when they would again test the surrounding areas. Each time they tested they were looking for the "negative margin," a term I learned all too well and heard repeated over and over again.

The first surgery went well but when the doctor later ran the tests, he learned they hadn't quite gotten enough of the affected tissues. I think it was hard for him to tell me that they didn't get it all. I know it was disheartening to him each time and my heart went out to him because I knew how hard he was trying. I could see the disappointment in his eyes and face and, interestingly enough, I felt his pain. I could also feel his resolve to take the next step in the treatment. I know it was as strong as mine and together we moved forward. We weren't done. We weren't beaten and neither of us was going to quit.

I didn't know it at the time but there would be four more major surgeries, separated by about two weeks each time, just to get me to the point where we would have to make the big decision. That decision would be to remove the remaining areas, including my right breast. By now I was even more determined to survive and have more time on this earth with my daughter, Chanel, even if it meant removing both breasts.

Blessed with Cancer

Each time I came home from the hospital Chanel would ask me, "Did they get it all?" I was hopeful every time but I would later have to tell her that they didn't. It was so hard for me to say it but I think it had to be even harder for her to hear it. It was so tough on this young ten year old. She also had to wait to find out and each time the answer was no, she had to suck it up one more time, steel herself and put on her beautiful, smiling face. She always did and would once again start reassuring me that everything was going to be all right. Her strength was so incredible it brought me to tears to think I was so blessed with this incredible child, my wonderful young woman. I hope she knows how much her support meant to me through the whole experience.

After the third surgery I anxiously waited to find out the results. As I normally did, I went in to see the doctor so he could explain the outcome. When he walked into the room my heart sank almost immediately. He wasn't much of a poker player. I could see his disappointment in having to tell me one more time that they hadn't gotten it all. For a moment I physically and emotionally collapsed in despair. I had to sit down and take it all in. However, the feeling only lasted for a moment. Suddenly something came over me and my will to survive welled up and over-shadowed every other emotion and I blurted out, "*Take them both.*" I decided enough is enough, that life is too important and the breasts had to go. I was not defined by my breasts. I am a person of value and I have so much to give to life, and especially to my daughter. Surgery after surgery was no way to live and I wanted to live. I wanted it done and done as soon as possible. So we scheduled my day. My B-Day for "Breast Day" would be my V-Day for "Victory over Cancer Day." I believed it would be my day of victory over cancer. How could I believe anything else? I couldn't! I wouldn't!

Blessed with Cancer

As I discussed it with my doctor, I knew this was the best decision and my doctor agreed. It also turned out to be the best decision for the long haul. My doctor had previously explained that I had two strains of cancer. One was the kind that affected soft tissues and was relatively easy to resolve as long as we could remove all the affected tissues and the cancer hadn't traveled to other tissues in my body. The second strain was the kind that he called ductile. I don't know exactly what that means but as I understood it in my simple mind, this strain liked to travel through ducts in my body and was more difficult to contain. The concern was that, because it was ductile, even if we removed just the left breast and had negative margins there, it was very likely that the cancer would eventually, if it hadn't already, travel to my right breast. Then I would have to go through the pain and procedures all over again. We decided that the best possible outcome would be one more surgery, removing both breasts including associated muscles, lymph nodes and tissues. This, hopefully, would complete the process.

I didn't want this day to come but it had arrived anyway. When I woke up I had a different feeling than all the anxiety I'd been experiencing in anticipation of this sixth surgery. There was an unusual calm about me as I thought about the day and what was yet to come. I prayed and read some scripture from the Bible, then prayed some more. I took a shower to wake up and freshen up. I stood there drying off in front of the mirror for what seemed a timeless moment of reflection and stared at my bare chest and the post-surgery effects of what had already been done to my left breast. I thought back about all that had occurred and how life might have been different if I had been spared the attack by cancer. I was no longer in despair but had finally accepted what was, what is, and what will be and living was what I wanted now. I suddenly heard myself saying goodbye to both of my breasts. That's okay. It was time to say good-bye. I finished toweling off, brushed my teeth, combed my hair and prepared to head for the hospital.

Blessed with Cancer

One of my girlfriends spent the morning with me helping me to prepare myself, but in a fun way. She encouraged and helped me to treat myself extra special. I took my time getting dressed, trying to decide what to wear. All the while we were laughing and talking. It was fun and I was distracted for the morning. I had some time since I didn't have to be at the hospital until early afternoon, so after I was dressed I went to the bureau and packed my bras and swimsuits. I thought, "*I don't think I'll be needing these anymore.*" I turned to the closet and glanced over the dresses and tops that I thought I would never wear again, all the while praying that this time the doctor would get it all.

I made three phone calls before I left the house. The first was to my mom to tell her I love her. That was very important to me and I needed to say it again. I believe she needed to hear it as well. She was having her own struggles in life and I wanted her to know I cared. My second call was to dad to see if he was on his way from Seattle. He was, but was running late. Still, there was plenty of time and I was comforted to know he would be in time to take me to the hospital. Lastly, but most important to me, was to call my daughter, Chanel, and tell her how much I loved her. I was calm and confidence and able to hold back the emotion in order to assure her that everything would be okay. I knew it would. Today was my day.

I can't explain my euphoric state of mind but I was at ease about the whole upcoming ordeal. I was even okay with the idea that I might not make it through. That was not part of my plan but it was a possibility. They even make you sign all those documents at the hospital accepting the possibility that you may not survive. I don't know if it is the whole "total disclosure" issue in the event something happens or if they are preparing you. There is risk with any surgery. Regardless, what will be will be and I was totally confident that everything would be alright. How else could I approach surgery of this kind? I also knew that once I was checked into the

Blessed with Cancer

hospital I was totally at the mercy of the doctors and nurses who have dedicated their lives to doing everything they can to help people heal. I believed and trusted in them.

As I left the house on August 31st, the end of the month, in my mind I also thought of "the end of my cancer." It was a warm and beautiful northwest day and everything about it felt right. Perhaps knowing I was going into the kind of surgery that was going to change my life I had a whole new perspective and saw the world differently. On this beautiful day, I chose to wear shorts and a tank top. I knew my outfits, at least for the next few days anyway, would be unattractive hospital gowns and loose clothing so I enjoyed my temporary freedom fashion statement. And, if I may be so bold to say so, I look really good in shorts and a tank top.

I got in my car and drove down the street to my retail business. There was time so I decided to check in with the gal that was going to cover for me while I was out of commission for the next few weeks. It was more about staying preoccupied before surgery than it was about needing to check on my shop. I was also waiting for my dad to arrive from Seattle to take me to the hospital. He wasn't as late as I thought and when he arrived we headed to the hospital.

When I walked through the entryway I knew this would be a big day. The next time I'd walk out these doors I would be a changed person, not only physically but mentally and emotionally as well. As I checked into the prep room I remember a momentary rush of anxiety. The nurses anticipated this and were ready for me. They were so caring and compassionate and made me feel at ease. They treated me like a princess, and like nothing else was more important than my comfort. They were awesome!

While I waited with family in the prep room the doctor came in to see me, as he always did before a procedure. He asked everyone to leave the room so we could have time together. When everyone was gone he went over the procedures and anticipated outcomes as he had done so many times before. This time he held my hand, looked me in the eyes and asked me "Are you ready?" I said I was. I could see tears welling up in his eyes. Over the past three months, as we prepared for this day, we had become good friends. We bonded and it was apparent that he really cared for me and my well being. I reassured him and told him that I'd trusted him this far and I trust that he will continue to take care of me. He promised that he was going to do his very best. Then he said, "Linda, you're one of the most courageous people I know. You are amazing! In all my years as a surgeon, you have shown the most positive attitude for this process and toward life of anyone I've ever taken care of." He also said that he was so sorry that this had happened to me. It seemed that he was feeling some level of guilt because he was going to have to remove both of my breasts. It wasn't his fault and, as promised, he had really tried to minimize the damage and save my breasts. I believed he was doing everything he could and now it was in the hands of my Heavenly Father, the Great Physician. This I truly believe.

Finally, the medicine they had injected to relax me began working and I was ready when they rolled me down the hallway and into the operating room. As they positioned the gurney I saw the bright lights above me and felt the cool, sterile atmosphere of the room as they moved me onto the operating table. I saw just a few masked people standing over me and, from that point forward, I don't remember anything. I thought that was a good thing. When I wake up, it will be all done.

I was still pretty much out of it but the first sound I heard as I began to regain consciousness was the faint and distant sound of an angelic voice. I wasn't able to move or open my eyes but I felt so safe as I struggled to understand what she was trying to tell me. I just wanted to fall back to sleep. Finally, I understood what she was saying. "Linda, try to take small breaths, not big ones." It was the recovery nurse helping me to wake up. I was so weak and, at first, I couldn't do anything, including respond. But she was patient and persistent and, as I fell in and out of sleep, I would hear her repeat: "Linda, can you hear me? If you can, wiggle your fingers." She kept calling my name. "Linda, I want you to try and take small, short breaths." She continued: "Yes, that's good, Linda. You are doing just fine. Keep them small. Linda, you are doing great!"

I don't remember everything but I vaguely recall a moment of clarity. While I was waking up and becoming more aware the doctor came into the recovery room to check on me. I heard his voice calling for me and I woke up as much as possible. I wanted to see him. I realized he was there as he stood at the foot of the bed tugging on my toes, something he always did following surgery. Then I heard those three wonderful words, "I got it!" he said with such relief in his voice. "I got it all!" All I could mumble was, "*I know. Thank you.*" Deep in my heart, even with all the fogginess of the anesthesia, I did know. My prayers had been answered.

I must have slept all day because I don't even remember being taken to my room. It seemed like days later but it was only that evening when I woke up with my best friend, Jody, sitting at my bedside. She had flown in from California to be here with me. I also remember my Aunt Becky being there to welcome me back. She worked at another hospital and understood what I was going through and came to be with me. The cards, flowers and fruit from so many caring people were a constant reminder of how blessed I was to have them all in my life. The visitors and occasional phone calls lifted my spirits and helped distract me from the pains of recovery. I especially enjoyed the visits and time spent with Chanel. I did this more for her than for me. I just loved to hear her voice and look into her smiling face. "You're doing really good, mom," she would say. "Keep it up. I love you."

Blessed with Cancer

Over the next few days, every time I woke up I was in horrible pain. They never told me it was going to be like this. "*Give me more morphine,*" I would plead but they could only give me so much. I remember the pain as the nurses reminded me to breathe lightly, like small little puffs of air. With all the stitches and binding it was very important that I didn't take any deep breaths. I only made that mistake once and realized why they were stressing the small breaths. I took that deeper breath and the searing pain was excruciating. It felt like my skin and muscles were tearing apart at the stitches and I imagined all the repair work the doctor would have to do to fix it. However, after my scream that brought nurses running and tears streaming down my face, the pain finally subsided and I was reassured by these gracious and gentle angels that everything was okay, and that I hadn't done any serious damage to myself. From that time forward I was very conscientious about my breathing.

I spent almost a week in the hospital recovering from the surgery. Tubes had been inserted just below my ribs on both sides of my body to allow drainage to take place during the healing. Even when I went home the tubes had to be cleaned on a regular basis so they wouldn't clog up and cause infection. The tubes were stitched into my sides and, because they were hanging out, I would sometimes accidentally hook them with the sleeves of my blouse or jacket. I cringed as a stab of pain reminded me they were still there and that I needed to be more careful.

With so many incisions infection was a constant concern. My wonderful 10-year-old daughter was such a trooper and helped me with the cleaning process. It seemed that nothing could rattle my little miss Florence Nightingale or her commitment to helping me. I choke up even now to think about how courageous and caring she was throughout the whole experience.

The next weeks and months, while healing and returning to normal life activities, I made my regular trips to the doctor for check-ups, cleanings, blood tests, therapy and evaluations. I

Blessed with Cancer

always enjoyed seeing my oncologist and hearing his warm and encouraging voice. I don't recall if I ever mentioned how handsome he was. No, actually, he was even better looking than just handsome. Some would even say he was "dreamy." I always looked forward to seeing him and was probably motivated to stick with the process because of who he was. We had developed such a warm relationship. Oh my goodness! I think I may have had feelings for him, although we both maintained a very professional doctor-patient relationship. It would be easy for me to have fallen for the man that was saving my life and looking so incredible while doing it. That is probably a story for another time.

After a couple of months my chest was finally healed. The drainage tubes were removed and the holes, while leaving more scars, healed nicely as well. Now, when I stood in front of the mirror I could see what it took to remove all the cancer from my body and save my life. The scars were still numerous and dark, carefully placed across my skin where my breasts had been just weeks earlier. My chest no longer displayed round, firm breasts, but was now slightly sunken, giving a concave appearance. Muscles had been removed along with my breasts and those that were left were stretched and strategically placed to retain their usefulness. Even to this day I have some limitations on their strength and what I can do with them but I have full use of my arms, shoulders and torso muscles. In fact, you probably couldn't tell which muscles are missing by looking and I have since rebuilt some of them to keep my natural form. The doctor and his team of nurses did such a skillful job and I am grateful for their work.

My chest was not attractive to look at and even caused me to occasionally stare. It wasn't that it was even repulsive. It just didn't look right. But I was adjusting and was happy to be alive. I'd said earlier that my breasts didn't define me and that is true. I was content the way I was, even after the numerous operations, and was in no hurry to take the steps to begin reconstructive surgery to make them look normal again. A few of my friends recommended I go to a specialty store and purchase some prosthetic breasts so I would look more normal and not so flat. Other well-meaning friends encouraged me to consider reconstructive surgery. Some even went on to say they thought I was enjoying the attention of being different. That wasn't it. At the time it wasn't that important to me. Part of why I didn't want prostheses was because I was more concerned about one day bending over and having them pop out of the bra in some public place. Can you imagine? The thought of that happening, whether it was even possible along with the accompanying humiliation or embarrassment, prevented me from taking that step. No! It just wasn't important. I was alright just the way I was.

After about nine months, though, I was ready for reconstruction. There was a lot of work to be done and it eventually took two surgeries to rebuild my breasts, including creating new nipples. The implants were added and the skin was masterfully and appropriately placed. In addition, the skin was manipulated to create two nodes to simulate nipples. After they healed, a good friend of mine finished the masterpiece by tattooing areolas around the nipples. It is amazing what was accomplished by each of the artists, including the doctor and his team of nurses. Today, they look very real and quite normal. Except for the remaining scars, most people couldn't tell. One more time I am blessed with success by so many committed professionals.

As time went on and I continued my recovery, I had a growing confidence and a new assurance that life was good and I would have the opportunity to live it to its fullest. There are no guarantees following cancer surgery and I'm occasionally reminded that others have not been so fortunate. I survived mine but there would still be milestones along the way that I would have to reach before I could be considered completely cured. Those milestones would come and I

Blessed with Cancer

would celebrate each time I reached one. I would also reflect back on how blessed I was to be alive and to have this chance. I did what I had to do to get through the numerous surgeries and survive. Oh, for sure, I had the occasional pity party for myself and experienced periods of depression but I never stayed there for very long. My family and closest friends wouldn't let me. They checked on me regularly and rallied around during the most difficult times to keep me looking up and moving forward. I developed a different mind set and committed to find the best life has to offer every day, regardless of the obstacles or the occasional set-backs. This was just a season of my life, although the most difficult I can recall, and there would be so many more bright and beautiful seasons to experience. The challenges weren't over but I was ready and on my way.

Chapter 4 – My Angel In A White Coat

"The human condition is the essential ingredient. It is only in the giving of oneself to others that we truly live." Ethel Percy Andrus

The first time I saw him I thought, "Wow, that's my cancer doctor? He's so young and so handsome." I'd also been told he was a brilliant doctor and very skilled in his field. Now, if you're a woman you may be wondering what he looked like. My girlfriends certainly wanted to know. He was tall, probably six foot three or four inches, and thin. He wasn't skinny but was physically-fit thin, with broad shoulders. His hair was dark brown and his face had soft, chiseled features. He was well-dressed and, clean-shaven, and if I may say so, had perfect lips. Yes, I noticed. You may not believe me but I am telling you how I remember him. The way he dressed was conservative and professional but current in style. His beautiful eyes were warm and caring and his soft-spoken voice was both welcoming and reassuring. My cancer doctor was so strikingly handsome, with a beautifully-stunning, model-perfect smile, that I believe he could have just walked off the front cover of the current issue of Gentlemen's Quarterly magazine. Sounds too good to be true, doesn't it? But, it was true. I had just met him but was looking forward to this relationship.

My mind was thinking, "This is going to be nice, and maybe even fun." However, he was focused on more important things. I could tell by the look on his face that he had something pretty serious to tell me. He asked me if I had a partner. I said "*Why?*" I thought that was a strange question. I'd just met him. Then I realized he was asking me if I had a group of supporters to help me through the experience that was to come. Do I have a spouse,

Blessed with Cancer

children....what family members do I have? I told him I had a 10 year old daughter. He asked if that was the only family I have here. I told him I'd moved down from Seattle, Washington, where I had left my family. He then went on to get to the point.

"As you well know, you'd found a lump in your left breast and it was removed during this last procedure. We've had it biopsied and I am sorry to have to be the one to tell you this but you do have breast cancer. Unfortunately, the lump is not benign and is indeed a threat to your life." My happy mood changed instantly as those words echoed in my mind. "You have breast cancer!"

As I thought about those words, he must have known what was going through my head. I'm sure I was not the first woman he has had to present this diagnosis to. He was direct but he was also gentle. It was as though he scripted his announcement to my specific personality and presented it in such a way that I could carefully absorb it. At one point he stopped and looked into my eyes and paused, as if thinking how to present his next comment. This must be important, I thought, and didn't know if I needed to prepare myself for what was to come. I waited patiently in anticipation of what he was going to say. His job must be very difficult at times, especially where he has to share these kinds of things with his patients. He wants to say it in just the right way in order to help the patient see hope in what was to come but also for them to understand the serious nature of their condition in order to prepare them for the next step.

Then he said it. "Linda, you are going to have to decide right now!" His emphasis was on those last three words, "decide right now." "You are going to have to decide right now that you are going to survive your cancer. You have to decide that you are going to beat it and nothing is going to distract you from that focus." I don't recall his exact words but what he said was that I would have to prepare myself mentally, physically, spiritually and emotionally for the fight. I think he wanted to know where I was regarding the challenge ahead and whether or not I was willing to do everything possible to survive. As I thought about it and only for a moment, not really understanding what all would be involved, I looked back at him and said that I would. I told him that I am prepared to do whatever it takes to survive. The doctor was visibly surprised and told me that he had never had a reaction as quick as that before. I went on to explain that I'd experienced another person going through this before in her 18-month battle but she didn't survive. She had lost her life at age 36 and left behind two young boys. I told him that I'd already decided and that I didn't want her end to be the end of my story. I want to do everything, and anything, to survive. I have a young daughter and I want to see her grow up. I want to spend time with her, being her mother and her friend, and I am not ready to just let it all go. I am not a quitter. I am a survivor. The doctor was pleased to hear me say this.

I told him I was prepared to have both of my breasts removed right now, whatever it takes. He said "No, not yet. We have other options." This was just the first of many appointments to come. My handsome doctor and I were going to be spending a lot of time together over the coming months. That, for me, was a pleasant revelation.

During one of my initial visits I asked the doctor if I could bring my daughter, Chanel, in to see him so that he could better explain to her about breast cancer and the process of this journey I would be on. Chanel had been with me while my friend, Annette, went through her treatments and the outcome that Chanel experienced was that Annette didn't survive. It was important to me and the whole process that the doctor explain to Chanel everything he explained to me. I wanted to instill in her the same confidence I had in my doctor. In doing this, he could give her the assurance and hope that I was going to be okay. I was going to make it. I believed it and I wanted Chanel to believe it too.

Blessed with Cancer

My next appointment was at the doctor's office to learn the results of my first surgery, the removal of the tumor. I was excited for two reasons. One, I believed I was going to learn that they had gotten the tumor early enough that it was all removed and life would be back to normal and perfect again. Two, I was going to get to see my really handsome cancer doctor. Going to see Dr. Eubanks was something I actually looked forward to. It even became a joke amongst my girl friends. I would tell them how really cute he was, how smart he was and how much fun we had during my visits. Don't get me wrong, he was always the consummate professional. He was also very positive and encouraging and each visit was an uplifting experience. It was hard to believe, with all things considered and the potential gloom that surrounded my condition that I looked forward to my visits. That may sound strange but I was just enjoying the distraction.

When I went into the doctor's office again I learned that he didn't get all the cancer. I was horribly disappointed and discouraged. I was looking forward to hearing that the surgeries were over, and that was the end of it. But, once again, that wasn't the case. I took a long, deep breath and pulled myself together. What is it going to take? I'd already decided that question so it didn't really matter what it would take or how many times I would go through this brief disappointment. I was committed to doing whatever I had to do to survive. So, what now? Robert said the next surgery would have to be more aggressive.

Yes, I did call him Robert. When I first met him, Robert was Dr. Eubanks. I think he really wanted to put me at ease so he asked me to call him Robert. I was perfectly happy to call him Robert and for him to call me Linda. He was such a wonderful person and genuinely cared so much about me and what I was going through. I suspect he was like that with all his patients but I wanted to believe it was about me. He was sensitive to my pain, all my fears and he wanted to do everything within his power to put me at ease and to help me survive. Robert was also exceedingly patient with my constant barrage of questions. I needed all the answers and help I could get to beat this beast called Breast Cancer. Robert created a professional, yet comfortable, environment for me so I could relax and be myself. Because of his approach, and our relationship, I was able to be open in all respects and get the help I needed. The passion for his work and compassion Robert had for his patients and their suffering was powerful. Personalized care doesn't get any better than this.

I am going to share something that I have previously shared with only one other person until now. It is rather personal and I understood what Robert was saying. I didn't want to share his comments before now for fear of sounding like I was boasting and that is not my intent. I'm telling you this story now because over the years I finally realized the anguish Robert must have been feeling each time I went into surgery.

During one of my earlier visits to the doctor during my preparatory exams, Robert said something to me that at first was a little embarrassing but flattering at the same time. As Robert examined my breasts to better understand my illness he commented that I had "perfect breasts." He went on to explain that he really meant what he had said. He said, "Linda, you really do have perfect breasts," with an emphasis on "perfect." I didn't know where he was going with this comment. He went on to explain that in his many years as a doctor he had examined hundreds, or more like thousands, of breasts, and that he had seen them in all colors, shapes and sizes in a number of variations of health. He again said that mine were perfect. I realized the dilemma for him was that during his effort to remove the tumor and save my life, he was going to have to cut into them to remove the threatening disease. In the beginning, with the initial invasive surgery Robert felt he could minimize the damage to my "perfect" breasts to the point where the visual impact would mostly be undetectable. However, when the first procedure didn't get all of the

39

Blessed with Cancer

cancer, I could tell that it was something Robert was struggling with more and more. With each successive surgery I could see the fear and anguish in his eyes as he tried to conserve my breasts in their natural form while trying to remove the remaining cancer. I was less concerned with how my chest would look following the surgeries and more concerned that I survive the disease. I know Robert was also concerned that I survive and was doing everything humanly possible utilizing his training, skills and years of experience to achieve that outcome. Yet, I think he also had a personal goal and confidence that drove him to want to be successful while keeping the natural physical beauty of my chest as close to perfect as possible. With the advance of the cancer and the urgent need to be more aggressive with my surgeries, I know it was a personal burden that he struggled with. He did everything he could and I know that if he could have preserved my breasts, he would have. I know he did what he could and I am grateful for his devotion to professionalism and especially to the well-being of his patients.

Having experienced it myself, I am confident that everyone who goes through some major illness in their life, whether it is their own illness they have to deal with or with that of a very close friend or loved one, they learn quite a bit about the illness and what causes it. In most cases, as I did, they probably feel they'd learned more about that illness than they ever thought they would have to or need to. You know what I am talking about. Well, here's just one little bit of information I learned which may help you understand why you are looking for a lump when you have a breast exam.

When the body is attacked by cancer it attempts to control the spread of the disease by surrounding it in a tumor. The tumor is like a protective capsule which the body creates in an attempt to contain the disease. The purpose of my first surgery was to remove the capsule and the cancer that was contained inside. Unfortunately for me, as it sometimes happens, the cancer had already managed to get outside of the tumor and infect my surrounding tissue. The second surgery was an attempt to capture all the remaining cancer, or affected tissues, before it spread too much further into my system.

With the second surgery Robert had to take more tissue in an attempt to get what they call a "negative margin." This is where the doctors remove affected tissue until there are no more cancer cells among the healthy ones. Surgeries usually last a few hours each. I prayed to God a lot, not only for me but for those who were helping me. I had to put my trust in these medical professionals who were doing everything their training had taught them to help me survive this disease. I was on the team and was cheering them on, for my sake. However, although my trust was in these professionals, my faith was always in God.

Prayer was a constant for me during this time. When I prayed I would ask God to help me and give me the courage to deal with this hand I've been dealt. I was scared and had many questions and I needed Him to turn to, to be there when I didn't have the strength to go on. There were too many unknowns. God knows all things and He knows the future. He knew what I would need. It's not surprising at all that God brought Dr. Robert Eubanks into my life. Robert would patiently listen to my concerns and gently explain the choices I needed to consider. This took extra time which he gave willingly. He would even call me at home to make sure I understood and we made "next step" decisions together. He also gave me his phone number so I could call him if I needed to talk or just ask questions. One time, Robert found a clever way to distract me which helped keep me from always focusing on my illness. For example, when I'd walk into his office he would ask an off-the-wall question like, "Where did you get that outfit?" At first I thought that was an odd thing to ask but, fairly quickly, I realized he was helping me take my mind off the cancer and the appointment. It worked! As time went on I became more conscious about what I was wearing when I went to my appointment, knowing that he would ask. He was pretty smart that way and I think wise beyond his years. He knew that clothes and shoes were important to me and that I always wanted to look professional and together. It wasn't an ego thing but more about image. Although I was a single mom running my own business I wanted to look and be successful in all parts of my life. Robert also knew I needed to have a positive attitude and the determination that I would survive and go on with my life as a successful business woman and mother. .

Robert was very special in his commitment to helping me. He knew everything he did was important to my recovery so he would do extra special things to help me. They were little things but hugely important in helping strengthen my confidence in him and my will to get better. I can best illustrate this with another example. One of the "little things" he would do while I was waiting in the pre-op area before going into surgery was to be sure to come in and see me. He would stand next to the gurney, take my hand and squeeze it. He would look directly into my eyes, making sure I could see him clearly, and spend a few minutes talking with me. I know he was reassuring me that everything would be okay. As he was leaving to get ready for the surgery, he would brush his hand on my leg from my knee down to my foot and he would wiggle my toes as one more signal of reassurance from the doctor to the patient that everything would be okay. At that point, I was ready.

Over the next few months I went on to have four more surgeries in an attempt to get all the cancer. The time passed so slowly and each time I was hopeful that it was the last time. I also had my moments of despair, tired of the pain of each surgery and the weeks of healing. Fortunately, I was blessed with a great support system of family and friends, an amazingly talented and caring doctor and my wonderful daughter, Chanel. She was the primary reason I couldn't let myself give up or quit. I also had my faith, a critical element in my formula for life. My hope was in my God, and the knowledge that He promised never to leave me, "For I will be with you always." I believed it, and now I know it.

During the very last surgery, as I was coming to, I had still not reached a full conscious level but I had a wonderful revelation. Although I couldn't move or respond to the directions by the nurses a realization came over me that literally filled my soul with joy. I felt like I was lying on a warm, puffy cloud, totally safe and content, when I knew with a certainty that the cancer was GONE! Although I was still asleep and weak I was conscious enough to feel the presence of my doctor standing over me and speaking in his soft voice. He said "Linda, I got it." I took a deep breath and somehow found the strength to whisper back, "I know."

Two weeks later, when I went to my follow-up appointment, I walked through the door of Robert's office and we saw each other. Without saying a word, we looked right at each other and broke into huge, uncontrollable smiles which immediately turned to laughter. We knew we had won and we shared the thrill of the victory together. This was our moment and only those who had given so much to the effort could really understand the joy that we were sharing. God was faithful to each of us in the way that we needed Him. As He promised, He gave me no more than I could handle.

Robert shared with me another very exciting piece of information. He had just learned that he was also cancer free. This was wonderful news because right in the middle of my series of surgeries I had learned that Robert was also being treated for his own case of cancer. As I learned earlier, he had had surgery and was going through chemotherapy and radiation treatment. He was dealing with all of this during the time he was working so hard to help me beat my cancer. I was so touched that he would share his story with me which only strengthened my appreciation for him. Robert and I were connected in an incredible and very special way and his strength gave me the courage to fight on.

I later learned that Robert was diagnosed again with cancer and I was concerned for him. I needed to share some thoughts with him. Actually, it was more of a regret that I had. I wrote a letter to Robert and gave it to one of his colleagues to give to him. In the letter I expressed how much I appreciated all that he had done for me and wished I could give back to him some of the encouragement and wise words that he'd so frequently given to me. I was, without question, forever grateful to him and all that he had done. My regret was that I hadn't shared my true feelings for him. I wanted him to know how my feelings for him had grown beyond admiration and appreciation and that I cared deeply for him. At the time I never said anything because I wasn't sure how things were going to turn out so I kept my feelings close and unexpressed. Still today that is one of my regrets. Maybe things could have been such that we could have shared some of our lives together but now we'll never know. It's at these times in my life when I am reminded that God has a plan for my life and His timing is always best. I don't know if Dr. Eubanks ever received my letter, or if he even felt the same way, but I needed to write it and send it to him. My heart would have it no other way.

A year later I learned that Robert was again diagnosed with cancer but this time it was a different type. I also found out that Robert's condition was such that he wasn't going to survive. I wasn't prepared for this. Robert was such an important person in my life. He had helped me through a very difficult time and he saved my life. It just couldn't be that, once again, I'd lost another good friend to cancer. It broke my heart to know that this wonderful man who had given so much of himself to help me survive my cancer had finally succumbed to the deadly disease himself. Not too much later, Robert was gone. I will never forget him. He is one of the true

Blessed with Cancer

heroes in my life, a blessing that I will always hold close to my heart. For me he will always be

remembered as my angel in a white coat.

Chapter 5 - Annette

"True friends are those who really know you,
but love you anyway."   Edna Buchanan

It's interesting how relationships in life come to us from some of the most unexpected places and, sometimes, through the most bizarre of circumstances. I'm sure you have experienced that yourself at times. You can't always know how something is going to turn out or, really, the full impact of the end result. That's one of the exciting elements that life brings, the special surprises we can't predict. If we prejudge a person or the factors surrounding a present relationship we may limit the blessings that come with the possibility of a new friendship. I have to admit there are times when we just don't want a relationship with some people. It's not about prejudging or about having preconceived ideas of what is going on in their lives or why you feel the way you do about them. Sometimes it may just be the result of our environment and the circumstances that bring these people into our lives. Most of the time we have no control over the people that God brings into our lives and we don't have a say about when or why. He has a plan, whether we are ready for it or not. Our choices are that we can fight it, deny it, ignore it and be frustrated or controlled by it. Or we can accept it, embrace it, or, in today's vernacular, we can "go with it." These are the exciting choices God gives us. If we weren't willing to do this we'd be in constant struggle with a bigger plan. Being only human, we try to control our destiny. But we eventually learn that we are more in control when we go with "whatever" God has planned for us. I haven't always felt that way, and in time, God reveals what we are to learn through this relationship. Call it a blessing in disguise.

Blessed with Cancer

Annette was the ex-wife of my husband and the mother of two handsome young boys, Timmy and Tyler, whom I was now raising. We'd been married just over seven years and I had known Annette most of that time. We never did get along and I didn't really understand why. Maybe it was just bad chemistry or maybe it was because I was married to her ex-husband and raising her two boys. It would have made more sense for her to dislike me if I'd had something to do with their break-up but, since I didn't know them at that time and had nothing to do with it, I never understood why our relationship was the way it was.

Annette only lived a few blocks from our home and was able to visit the boys pretty regularly. In my mind, it was probably too convenient for her to be able to come over so often. For the most part, when she did interact with the family we both did our best to keep the relationship about raising the boys, with me having step-mom responsibilities and Annette having birth-mom responsibilities, but on an inconsistent basis. A friend once told me that a movie had been made about our story and I asked her what movie that was. She said that if anyone had seen the movie "Step-Mom", starring Julia Roberts and Susan Sarandon they would have a pretty good idea of our relationship. I was trying to be a "good" mom, raising Timmy and Tyler in such a way as to not replace their mom but to give them the on-site mother every child needs. It was a really sensitive balancing act to not only meet the needs of these two boys, whom I loved like my own, but to also include my own daughter, Chanel, whom I also loved so much. Being all things to everyone, including my husband, three dogs, a cat, a fish, a house and a business was not easy. Just keeping up with the three kids, who each attended a different school with different schedules, sports activities and individual hobbies was, at times, a bit much. I sometimes felt that there must have been three of me. It all happened so fast. You know how these things run together. Some of you are living a similar life, with similar challenges, right now. My advice is

48

Blessed with Cancer

to hang in there but stay focused on the things that are most important. To me those things are faith, family, health and career, in that order. On top of all of this, I was trying to accept and maintain a workable relationship with the involvement of the boys' mom, Annette. This relationship may have been the most difficult of everything going on in my life.

Annette was thirty-six years of age at the time and had some personal challenges of her own in life. Our relationship, although mostly cordial, had been plagued with years of verbal and emotional abuse, mostly directed at me. I imagine that some of her anger, maybe even bitterness, was a result of having lost her husband to divorce and, thus, losing the privilege of daily contact with her boys. She loved Timmy and Tyler dearly but circumstances were such that she was no longer able to be a regular part of their life. That must have been very difficult and, in some ways, I can sympathize with what she was going through. My patience with Annette's constant personal attacks was really stretched at times. She was quite skilled at trying to harm me with her clever, and mostly subtle, comments and actions.

We were celebrating Chanel's sixth birthday with family and some of Chanel's close friends. As always, Annette made her presence known. She loved to be the center of attention. On this, Chanel's special day, I didn't respond as well as I possibly should have when Annette crashed the party and took the attention away from Chanel. I slipped into my protective-mother mode and reacted to her intrusion. You can visualize the lioness and her response when her cub is in danger. I was on it in a flash. Annette was somewhat taken aback when I grabbed her by the arm and escorted her out of the house and down the walkway to the street and off the property. It surprised me to some degree because I weigh about one hundred one pounds soaking wet and am five feet one inch tall. Annette, on the other hand, was five feet seven inches, weighing in at about one hundred and forty-five pounds. The amazement to me was that I could move her at all, especially as she resisted. However, you know the power of a mother and what she will do to protect her young.

When we reached the street I released my grip and Annette spun around and slapped the sunglasses off my face. She then grabbed my tank top and ripped the strap off one shoulder. *At that point, I'd had enough. I poked her in the eyes, kicked her in the groin, pulled her shirt up over her head and drop-kicked her into the street.* No, I really didn't do that. I'm not that kind of a person. However, it is how I felt and what I had briefly visualized in my mind. You know how it is when, afterwards, you always think about what you wish you had said or done. What did happen, though, is that Annette left and, except for a brief return later that evening, it was pretty much over. During the next few months she would call me and make threats over the phone. Mostly, it was intimidation and the threat that she was somehow going to hurt me. I really felt that she meant to say something more serious and threatening but managed to stop short of anything that would cause me to contact the police. A more serious or specific threat could have meant jail time for her. A few months later, a full-grown pumpkin was thrown through our double-plated bedroom window. We didn't see who did it but we had a good idea who it might have been.

I believed that Annette had a vengeance for me. For a long time, she would vacillate between attacking me on some occasions, and attacking my husband at other times. This included phone messages to my husband to set up meetings to discuss the boys. What she was doing, in fact, was using these meetings as a way of placing a wedge between my husband and me. Although Annette was no longer married to the person who was now my husband, we still included her in activities with the boys. She was part of a blended family. As you can imagine, blended families sometimes have challenges that are fueled by former relationships. However,

Blessed with Cancer

we agreed that it would be good for both Annette and the boys to have a relationship with one another. Even though she made it very difficult for almost eight years, we managed to keep our marriage together and lead somewhat normal lives, with minimal impact on the children.

I realize I have gone into some detail about the negative side of my relationship with Annette and with some of the challenges that we faced on a regular basis. Believe me, there were times when there was no love lost between us. The attacks and defenses were all too frequent, at least so it seemed, and there were sometimes when I thought it would never end. I need to share this with you so you will better understand what I am going to tell you next. Life's direction can change in an instant, a moment or heartbeat. Suddenly things as we know them, or think we know them, will completely change direction. This creates a new paradigm, a new reality for everyone within the sphere of influence of those involved. We didn't know it but one was about to occur that would impact us all.

About nine months later, in March of the following year, my husband got a call that changed my life forever.......he learned that Annette had been diagnosed with breast cancer. This was going to affect all of us. During the next few months, Annette went through surgery, chemotherapy and radiation treatments. No one should have to endure this process but tens of thousands of people do all the time. To survive, and hopefully beat this beast, it was something Annette had to do. We were all concerned, including me. Something like this sheds a whole new light on people, circumstances and life in general. It was a long struggle for all of us.

One person who was profoundly impacted was my own daughter, Chanel. I'm so proud of her and who she is. I sometimes refer to Chanel as the sweet, squishable, purple girl (she really loved the color purple). *I also sometimes refer to her as Boo Boo, Shaw Shaw, Nellie, Little Doll, Honey and Number 5. (You know, like Chanel Number 5)* When Chanel learned about

Blessed with Cancer

Annette's condition she took it upon herself to do something special and encouraging for Annette, who also loved purple. Each week Annette would have to go for her radiation treatments and every week Chanel would bring her something special always in some shade of purple. This went on for months. Chanel would bring her balloons, candles, candy, cards, body splash, lavender stationery, decorated wine bottles, nail polish, flowers and other little purple gifts. I was so impressed and blessed by my daughter's compassion and commitment to bring some joy into Annette's life through these small gestures. It was my responsibility to drive Chanel each week to visit Annette and, through this process, I learned even more about love and compassion for another suffering human being. It helped me to see Annette in another light and things would change because of it. Over time, my relationship with Annette did change. I felt that I, too, could do more to help her through her treatment and recovery. I learned to listen more, to focus more on her struggle and less on my little challenges. By doing this, I was able to discover ways I could help her. Here's just one example:

During remission Annette had made mention she had always wanted to be a flight attendant. I had been a flight attendant for 10 years with a major airline and I was able to help her realize that dream by helping her write a resume. I was able to help her land an interview through my professional friends. Now it was up to Annette. Prior to this time, she had pretty much always been a young, stay-at-home mother and this was a whole new experience.

Annette went through the interviews and the training and qualified with flying colors. She was on her own and out into the "friendly skies" she went. However, after just two trips she decided that was all she could handle. We were all somewhat surprised that her new career was over so soon. This had been her dream. We all thought it was probably because she had gone through so much during her cancer treatments but we later learned that it was something much more than that, something we really didn't expect…something we never would have imagined.

One day, what seemed out of the blue and contrary to what we knew as normal behavior for her, Annette called me and invited me to go with her on a weekend trip to Bend, Oregon. Can you believe it? I couldn't. I had some doubts regarding her motive for asking me. With all she and I had been through, you too are probably wondering why I would even consider going off alone with this woman. This was different. We were former adversaries now going off for a weekend of bonding? It was to be a "just for the chicks" trip. My husband, as well as the rest of the family, told me that I shouldn't go. Annette had not been very nice to me for many years and going off for a weekend alone with her was the craziest thing they had ever heard. No one was in favor of it, including me. I struggled with the idea. As a matter of fact, one night I woke up in a cold sweat just thinking about it. It occurred to me that God was trying to tell me something. When He speaks to your heart, you don't always understand or you aren't sure that it really is God speaking to you in this way. However, the feeling that I had was that if I didn't go I would be sorry. This decision, as many do, needed extra prayer. There must be a reason and I had to find out what this was about. After a couple of days I called Annette back to say yes and we started planning the trip. When I said I was going everyone thought I was out of my mind. Perhaps, but this is something I felt I had to do. In fact, I believe I was listening to God. He had something else in mind and I needed to find out what that was.

Annette and I packed our stuff for a weekend and headed out in Annette's car for beautiful Bend. We started talking from the time we walked out the front door and talked constantly all the way there. It was just like we'd known each other all our lives and were best friends. That's what was so odd. We didn't and we weren't. But something was changing between us and I felt it was good. The trip was about a three and a half hour drive from our home in Gresham, Oregon over the pass and under the shadow of majestic Mt. Hood and then south to Bend. Who knew we had so much to talk about!?

We arrived in Bend, checked into our hotel room, had some refreshments and went straight to the pool. I think we were both pretty nervous. Annette and I both love the sun and it gave us a chance to relax, enjoy the warmth and get to know each other better. Oh, my gosh! It was totally unexpected but we both acted like long-lost sisters. We found out that we had so much in common. It was really fun, and being alone together made it possible for both of us to really open up and share with each other.

We went back to our room and got ready to go out to dinner. Annette went into the bathroom to dress and I stayed in the bedroom. We hadn't previously talked about what we should wear but when Annette came out of the bathroom we looked at each other and started laughing. It was hilarious. We were both wearing Franco Sarto black slip-ons (sandals), black short sleeve shirts and 501 button-up Levi jeans. We almost looked like twins, only one short and one tall. *Remember, I'm the short one.* We went off to dinner still laughing about how we are so much more like each other than we had even realized. As newfound friends we continued to laugh together all weekend. There were times that we laughed so hard our cheekbones hurt. Wow, did I have fun!

Throughout the evening we danced, we laughed and, occasionally, we even fought off the advances of some gentlemen at the club. It was easier than I imagined because once they found out that I was the step-mom of Annette's boys and that she and I were married to the same man (thankfully, not at the same time) they didn't choose to stick around and hear any more of our

Blessed with Cancer

bizarre stories. It wasn't quite an all-nighter but it was close. We finally went back to the hotel and to sleep.

When we got up in the morning we had breakfast, put on our swimsuits and went out to the pool again. This time we talked mostly about our kids and how much they meant to both of us. Little did I know what was coming. Annette had told me she loved my daughter, Chanel, and I know that Chanel loved her as well. She also knew that I loved her boys, Timmy and Tyler. Then Annette asked me a question which I thought was interesting and caught me off guard. No, actually, it was odd. I thought we were talking about our children, and suddenly Annette asked me, "What is your five-year plan?" The question seemed so off-the-wall I think I was giggling when I kind of whimsically threw the question back to her. "What's yours?" She said, "No, really! I am serious, what is your five-year plan? I said "The same plan I have been on and that is to raise the kids." She seemed to lay back, with a look of reassurance on her face. I then realized that she <u>was</u> talking about the children. What she was doing was actually passing the baton from mother to mother, from her to me and letting me know that what I was doing was right and that she was good with it. She was also trying to tell me something that I didn't yet fully comprehend.

We enjoyed the rest of the weekend together. We golfed, had lunch, went back to the hotel to watch TV and rest, ate junk food together and just enjoyed our new friendship. When Annette fell asleep while we watched television, I thought long and hard about the conversations we had had earlier in the day. She was trying to tell me something. She hadn't yet laid it out in clear simple words but I think I was figuring it out.

We got up the next day and headed home to pick up the three kids, Annette's boys and my daughter. Part of what was becoming clear to me is that Annette was ill. I didn't know how ill until later. I saw a symptom of that on the way home when, on a couple of occasions, Annette would drive over the center lane and back and talk about the white spots she had seen. She was not making sense and this concerned me. After we'd picked up the kids and returned to our home we all had ice-cream together. Wow, what a dream come true. We were finally a real blended family. Annette, my husband, the three kids and me.

The next communication we had with Annette was a few days later when we found out that she had gotten into a fender bender while driving the boys to school. Everyone was okay, but following the accident Annette went home and went to bed, complaining of a headache. When she tried to get out of bed she was unable to walk correctly. She would walk into walls and was somewhat delusional, saying all kinds of things that made no sense. She went back to bed, never to get up again. We soon learned that Annette had cancer of the brain. Her breast cancer had metastasized to her brain, explaining her strange behavior.

There was somewhat mass confusion in our lives! Annette had no money and no insurance and was behind on her car payment, her house payment and most everything else. The uncertainty was affecting all of us. We needed to do something fast. The kids needed a diversion or, more correctly, an outlet to do something where they could help Annette, their mom. We talked about it and the kids decided that they could do a car wash. The first thing they did was make several beautiful signs in neon pink and lime green. How appropriate. For many people, pink is a healing color and is used as a symbol for those affected by breast cancer…. not just those who have it, or are survivors of it, but all those who care and help support these cancer victims. The boys made the signs in neon pink and themed their car wash as "A Car Wash for My Mom." This was just the beginning. I spoke to the principal at each of the local grade schools where Timmy, Tyler and Chanel all attended. Also, many of their friends were from the same school. They all jumped in to help us have a very successful event. People came from all around the community to support the wash. It was a huge success and brought a great deal of visibility to their cause.

It is so amazing what one simple project can turn into in the form of blessings. People in our community are so caring and it was touching to see all that came about because of the boys' efforts to do something practical to help their mom. The news media showed up to cover the story. People organized an effort to raise money to help offset the medical expenses and to provide financial support for the boys' future. At the encouragement of a friend, a very special final memory was created for the boys through the wonderful Making Memories Foundation. Annette wanted to give her sons their very own dirt bikes to ride, something they really loved to do. So many blessings sprung up and we were all touched by the generosity. It didn't prevent the loss of Annette but it brought us all much closer and made the boys feel that THEY had really done something special for their mom and they had. In the process, so many more people became aware of the threat of breast cancer and the devastating effect it has on the lives of those it touches. Annette didn't survive but her memory lives on in the hearts of all those she touched and those who rallied to help her.

For me, what had originally been an antagonistic relationship with a bitter, angry woman (maybe her, maybe me, but probably both) became a wonderful blessing with a real friend. Cancer had won again but only in the taking of her precious life. It also brought together two families and blended them into one. Love grew, relationships were healed and life's happy memories always overshadow the dark ones. In the end love does conquer all, including the devastating effects of breast cancer. Therein lies "the Blessing."

Chapter 6 – Chanel, My Chanel

"If you want to receive more from life,
simply give more to life."   Dr. Eric Allenbaugh

The greatest blessing of my life came to me on May 18, 1991 when my first and only child

was born. Wow, just moments earlier I was wondering if it was ever going to happen. I'd

carried this child for nine long months. I also wondered if the birthing process was going to kill

me. I can't say I really enjoyed being pregnant but I was ecstatic in anticipation of giving birth

to a child with whom I would share my life. At the time it didn't matter to me if it were a boy or

a girl, just that it would be healthy with all its fingers and toes. When she finally arrived and she

turned out to be a girl I was so overcome with love and appreciation I just wanted to hold her

forever. I believe I would have been just as happy if my baby had turned out to be a boy but I

think I was especially grateful that my first child was a girl. I already knew what it is like to be a

girl and to grow up as a girl. I thought that maybe this is where I should start as I learn to now

be a mother. What an awesome responsibility.

When it came time for me to deliver, the doctor decided that a normal birth was probably not

a good idea and that it would be best for me to have a C-section. I guess my tiny frame would

just not tolerate the natural process. I am so petite that one of my friends said that if you look up

the word "petite" in the dictionary, you'd see my picture. I doubt that but it was something we

laughed about. After all was said and done, the C-section was a good choice. When Chanel

joined the world she was all of nine pounds in weight and measured twenty-one and a half inches

in length. That explains a lot, including my relief to have her out my body and wrapped warmly

in my arms. There is no other experience like it, the most precious of all gifts.

Blessed with Cancer

Before she was born I actually saw her for the first time in a dream. In my dream I saw that she was going to be bald, with blue eyes, a big head and white, white skin. When I finally saw her, she had a head full of dark, curly hair (clearly her dad), bright red lips and olive skin. I think Chanel's skin color came from her great-grandmother who was full-blooded Iroquois indian from the Toppenish tribe. One of the first things I noticed was that her feet were also long and huge. I heard the nurses talking, and they were saying "Look at those feet. Those are toddler feet." They may have not said it quite like that. I think I was still under the influence of some powerful drugs so please don't hold me responsible for anything I think I may have heard at the time. Yes, I was awake but I was feeling no pain. Still, I believe I remembered every moment.

Giving birth to Chanel was a wonderful and life-changing experience. I'd already forgotten the long, final months and the eventual pain of the labor. God gave me this gift in the form of a beautiful child, a girl, and He entrusted me to care for her. At that moment I committed that I would take care of her and be the best mother ever. Wow! What a huge responsibility. Having a child really does change your perspective on life and helps you understand what is really important.

I remember the day I told Chanel I had cancer. We were wrestling on the bed and I was tickling her, a bonding thing I loved to do, knowing that she said she hated it. Although she claimed she didn't like to be tickled, I think she really enjoyed the physical touch and closeness of being with her mother. The horsing around was fun and the tickling was something she endured. It was a bonding moment that assured us both that we were alright and that everything is okay between us.

Trying to keep the moment light, I paused and said there was something I needed to tell her. Chanel had that look of, "*okay, but is this a serious 'something' or a kidding moment?*" As I

Blessed with Cancer

tried to read her face I thought, *"There is no gentle way to say it so just say it! Stop dragging this out!"* I looked at Chanel and told her I'd found a lump in my breast, that I had been to the doctor for tests, and that after receiving the test results he confirmed that I had breast cancer. I tried to assure her by saying the doctor also said that we had found it early and that it is something we could manage. That's not what he really said but I had to try to take away the worst fears that she might envision.

I told her I didn't fully understand all the details but what I was sure of was how hard I would fight. I wanted to instill in her the belief that everything would be okay. As I held her face in my hands and looked directly into her eyes, I promised her I would fight with every part of my being and with every ounce of my strength and unconquerable willpower to beat this. However, I would need her help.

I still remember the loss of color in her face and the distant look in her eyes. It was as if she had completely checked out. At that moment I could sense that she had gone somewhere else....so far away. The blank expression on her face made it impossible to read her thoughts and I got scared. Was I too straight-forward and was my honesty too much for her to handle? Did I ambush her with the most horrific thing I could have told her? That wasn't my intent but she needed to know and I needed for her to know. Our relationship was always that way... so up-front. We shared everything with each other.

As the process began and continued for many months, we worked together through doctor visits, bandage changes, too many medicines, trips to the hospital and running my business. At one point Chanel asked me if we had to go to any more doctor appointments. It was almost like the long trip we've all experienced when your child keeps asking, *"are we there yet,"* and you have to tell her, *"not yet...just a little longer."* All the while you just want to get there so the trip

Blessed with Cancer

will be over, and you don't have to keep saying, *"just a little longer."* I wanted the trip to be over as well, with a happy ending. That was my constant prayer.

I used to think, *"What a wonder child my Chanel was, literally."* Here's what I mean by that statement. During those long weeks and months I thought of her as my "wonder" child because it made me always wonder how, at 10 years of age, she was able to maintain such a wonderful spirit about her. I wondered why she wasn't going insane with fear and irrational anticipation that I might not make it. Annette didn't and Chanel knew her very well and what she had gone through, just to lose to her cancer. Maybe I was being a little naïve or maybe even backward. Perhaps Chanel was stronger than I imagined she should be and that experiencing the decline and eventual loss of Annette had prepared her to some degree. Chanel was experiencing what could have been viewed as a combination of seemingly life-threatening stresses. She was brought along through Annette's death, my second divorce, the loss of her stepbrothers, upheaval of our home after nine years and, now, my breast cancer ordeal.

There was also the amount of time and energy I had to put into my new specialty pet food business. In retrospect, this may have been one of the most positive parts of her life. Maybe this was the rock to which she clung, in some ways, because of all the animals. Animals, especially dogs, love so unconditionally and are always excited to see you and make you feel special. I believe there is real healing therapy through the association with animals. It may have been an escape for her or maybe it was just her natural strength that was so apparent to me but I was constantly amazed by her spirit and good will. I think it was another amazing miracle that, through it all, she was able to maintain her wonderful, uplifting spirit, great attitude and good grades. The most powerful blessing that I was able to enjoy was that Chanel and I maintained a wonderful and loving relationship between a mother and her daughter. .

Blessed with Cancer

I will never forget the days I would come home from either seeing the doctor or from having been in the hospital for another surgery and Chanel would ask, "Did they get it all?" Each time, I could see her eyes filled with hope that they had succeeded while at the same time fearing the answer would be the same that it had been the times before. I know she must have been struggling with so many questions while all along trying to maintain her composure and not show how she really felt. She wanted to be strong for me and tried so hard to be encouraging. "Mom, everything is going to be alright you'll see." As her mother, I knew and sensed her real fear. As hard as she tried, I kinda saw right through her. Still, I was so impressed how grown up she was and overwhelmed with her strength and courage. I just can't imagine going through what she was going through at her age. She was such an anchor for me and a great source of encouragement. Where did all that strength come from? She is the strongest young person I know.

Chanel would find things to do to keep her mind thinking in a positive light. One day, by accident mind you, I came across her online journal. I learned that journaling was one way she used to express what she was feeling and experiencing as she supported me. I also found that she developed a picture graph that she kept, kinda like a timeline, to help her track my progress as I dealt with my breast cancer. I didn't know she was doing this so when I found out it was a complete surprise to me. I wouldn't have thought of that myself and was so impressed that she had come up with such a practical tool to provide a report on my moods. Looking at it later, I was able to see Chanel's evaluation of my progress throughout the ordeal and better understand the depth of her caring and compassion for me. It also gave me a glimpse of the depth of her character to be so strong at such a young age.

Blessed with Cancer

Another way Chanel used to keep herself distracted was to write letters to the Bird Rescue. She later used what she learned to adopt a bird of her own and give it a home in our house. I think she had a plan all along. She also spent a lot of time drawing just about anything, but her real passion was for cats and dogs.

Chanel was a strong, young person more so than I knew but, in the process, I was learning. We moved to Gresham, Oregon, about the time Chanel finished her elementary grades and she had to go to a different school. She was one of the new kids and didn't know anyone. This is once again when her deep character showed through. The friends she had grown up with weren't there and Chanel was on her own to meet and make new friends. To do this, she looked around until she found someone else that was new to the school and didn't appear to have friends already and she made friends with them. In time she met other students and adjusted to the new school environment.

Another thing Chanel did to keep herself busy was to search the internet for puppies. This wasn't something she did all the time but something she started doing after I had to give away her pet puppy. There was a reason. I'm not a mean person, really.

A few years ago while we were dealing with Annette's cancer and subsequent death, her children were affected in many ways. This was a difficult time for her two sons and they became very mean to Chanel's dog. I'm sure it can be explained that they were just acting out their anger at the loss of their mother and that is no doubt true. However, I just couldn't allow that abuse to continue and because I was now even more responsible for helping raise the boys I felt it best that the puppy went to a new, safer home. Yes, it was hard and I had to explain it to Chanel in a way that she could accept. I explained the reasons for my decision and, with her approval, I gave her dog away to a family that would love him and treat him well. Once again she amazed me with her understanding and support, which I really needed. It hurt me to have to give the dog away, mostly because of how I thought it would affect Chanel. In spite of my concern I think she understood it was best for the puppy. Still, as a parent we don't want to do anything to hurt or upset our children and Chanel was such a loving, caring angel. She just knew. I don't know how at her young age but she did. In addition, when I developed breast cancer, dealing with it all was just too much for me. Giving the puppy away to a good home was the right thing to do and we both agreed. I promised her that when I beat this cancer I would get her a new puppy. That was good enough for Chanel so she kept busy searching for puppies on the internet.

Chanel went a step further and began to immerse herself in the process of learning everything she could. She spent time researching breeders, the puppies' history, types of food to feed dogs and other general information that proved to later be helpful to me when I opened my specialty pet food business.

Since she couldn't have a puppy until the battle was over she was very creative and went on line to also research bird rescues. She thought a bird might be easier for me as a first pet. She was only ten years old but she had accepted that when the time was right and when I was able she would get her puppy. What an incredible little lady. I was so amazed that her thoughts were always about me and what made my life better. In my observations Chanel's interests were never about her or what SHE needed. It was always about me. I am so blessed to have her in my life and thank God every day for her.

Chanel also had a real raw talent for drawing, and would use her art to make "get well" cards for me all the time. Somehow, during this period in our lives, she learned how to knit and crochet. She was always making scarves for me or for one of our friends or she was making hats for her nephews. She also made potholders and other little things like that. Although I was not

into knitting, when I saw her working so diligently and with such focus, I was impressed. I

thought, "*That is pretty cool for a ten-year-old.*" However, in all truthfulness and though this

was a temporary distraction, my focus was on my survival. I had to survive. I wanted more time

to be able to spend it with Chanel. That was most important in my mind.

Chanel had every reason to be afraid, angry and confused but somehow held herself together

for me. How would she know to do that? She focused her time and energy in ways to keep busy

and bring comfort and assurance to my life. I was fighting to survive and I think she was

fighting to help me survive. In one of those special and memorable mother-daughter moments

she told me she did not want me to have any storms or stresses in my life. She wanted things to

be calm, comforting and peaceful for me. At that moment I was no longer able to hold back my

tears. I was so overcome with gratitude and total admiration for Chanel as a person I just had to

hold her and sob. I was so proud of my baby, as any mother would be. She showed me such a

depth of character in her as an individual that I forgot she was only ten.

Just recently when Chanel and I were talking, I thought back over the years and what she and

I had been through and I asked her how she managed to stay so solid as a person. Considering

all things, she could have gone sideways with life. By that, I mean that she could have used all

those circumstances surrounding our lives as excuses to rebel, act out or blame life, the world or

God for what was going on. Nevertheless, she didn't. She was incredibly mature, focused and

she demonstrated such compassion for me and my fight that I believe God was using her to give

me hope and strength on a daily basis through her example.

During one of our sharing moments, Chanel told me there was a period of time when she was

sitting at school just observing, in her words, the "naughty girls." She saw the way they dressed, the way they flirted with the boys to get attention and even kissing those boys. Even the things they would say were somewhat shocking to her. For a while she thought about joining in. She had never behaved that way and wondered what it would be like. However, she told me she chose not to get involved with that crowd. It just didn't feel right. Chanel made a conscious decision to keep living her life according to the way she was raised. She saw no good outcome of that kind of behavior. It wasn't who she is. I don't know that this was part of her thinking but I want to believe it was. I really believe that in her heart she was thinking about me again and all that I was going through. I believe she didn't want to disappoint me or add one more hurt to my life. I just think that is her nature. I also believe she is my gift from God that shows me how much He cares for me. I have been so blessed and encouraged by her life, who she is and the young woman she is becoming. She is truly "God's girl." .

It's interesting when it is just the two of you facing life together and you can't drive, your daughter is only ten and you have no family in the area to help. You still have to keep on "keeping on." During that time and under the weight of all those challenges, Chanel and I became so close, and she seemed to grow up so fast. We had great respect for each other and our love grew out of places and circumstances we never would have imagined. Occasionally, the thought came into my mind that maybe she is an angel sent down to earth to be in my life, to give me purpose and to be a presence to help me through the most awful period of my existence. She is THE blessing of all the blessings in my life. To this day, and from the bottom of my heart, I believe that Chanel saved my life. God directed all of this but it was His gift of Chanel that made me determined to survive breast cancer. The decisions I made regarding going through all the pain of surgeries and the eventual removal of both of my breasts was the result of my decision to live...to survive...so I can spend many more years with my Chanel. There were

Blessed with Cancer

even times when I screamed out in anguish and despair a prayer for God to give me relief from all the pain. I even begged God on my knees, saying, *"please don't take Chanel's mom."* I could survive and endure any of the pain I had to go through if it meant I would have time on this earth to be with my daughter. I am convinced beyond any shadow of doubt that it has all been worth it. If you were to ask me if I could go back in time and if I had a choice to do it all over again, knowing the amount of pain I would have to experience, would I? The answer is, and will forever be... yes, Yes, YES! Chanel is worth it and God has promised never to allow us more than we can endure. His strength is sufficient and He will be with us always.

So much has happened over these years. Shortly, I will see Chanel graduate from high school and go on to college. God willing, I will see her graduate from college, go on to a career, meet a young man who will love and cherish her, they'll get married and they will eventually have a child of their own. I want to see all of that and more. When Chanel has a child, an angel like her, that will make me a grandmother and I am so OKAY with that. I will be honored to be granted that wonderful responsibility.

Chapter 7 – Making Memories

"If you put everything off until you're sure of it,
you'll get nothing done."   Norman Vincent Peale

Annette was dying. She knew it and many of us knew it as well. She had already accepted the fact that she was not going to survive her cancer so now all her focus was on her two young boys and what she could do to be with them more in the time she had left. She was no longer married to the boys' father and was therefore no longer directly involved in raising them. However, she continued to be part of their lives in as many ways as possible. This wasn't always a good situation, especially for the family get-togethers because I was the new wife, married to her ex-husband. Although she wasn't living with us, Annette wanted to continue to be the boys' mom and insert herself in their lives and upbringing. For many years this created problems for all of us, including some difficult and awkward moments but it was especially difficult for me because I was now raising her sons.

As all believers know, God can work in mysterious ways which He did when He brought Annette and me together for that weekend in Bend. It was there where she and I spent some one-on-one time together and developed a special bond and lasting friendship. Things had changed in Annette when she realized she had cancer and she was trying to repair some relationships and give more meaning to her life during whatever remaining time she had. At the same time, God changed my heart toward her. I could only imagine what she must have been going through which made me sympathize with her situation. I wanted to do everything I could to be her good friend, help her through her treatments, her hopeful recovery and do whatever possible to make her quality of life better. One way was to include her more in the lives of her sons and having

Blessed with Cancer

them more involved in her life. They needed to know this wonderful side of Annette so they could remember the special times.

On a number of occasions I spent time with the boys talking with them about their mother and trying to get a sense of what they knew about their mom's cancer and how they were dealing with it. Since, in addition to raising my daughter Chanel, I was also raising the two boys I felt it was important to help them understand what Annette was going through. At their young, pre-teen years of age this could likely be very difficult to comprehend and deal with. Pre-teens and teens seem to have so many challenges in their lives already, let alone being affected by their parents' divorce, a new step-mom and then the likely loss of their birth mom. I knew it would be difficult so I was concerned that they understand and take some steps to do what they could to help.

As I thought about what the boys could do to help, I was reminded of the growing medical expenses for Annette's cancer treatments and long recovery. Medical insurance only goes so far, and every little bit helps. More important though was the boys taking steps to be involved and doing something for their mother. It occurred to me that something they could do, with the help of family and friends, was put on a car wash. That they could do and the distraction for the boys was a perfect solution for them being busy and having a sense of doing something to help. I think it was therapeutic for all of us. Now there was a new focus and a purpose for our activities and we were able to engage so many other people in the effort.

I found a suitable location for the car wash, set the date and invited everyone who knew about Annette's situation to get involved in some way. It took organization and coordination but people were stepping up to help in some way or get involved by volunteering their time to help the boys wash cars. I even sent out an announcement to the local newspapers and television stations to tell them what the boys were doing. I was wonderfully surprised when so many

media organizations showed up to cover the event but I wasn't prepared for all the attention it

created around Annette, the boys and the family.

One of the television stations that covered the story of the car wash was the ABC affiliate

KATU, Channel Two in Portland. This was significant in that it was seen by a woman who runs

a national organization called Making Memories, which is also headquartered in Portland.

Making Memories, a non-profit charity, provides special memories for women and men who

have terminal breast cancer. Their mission is to create a memory, based on the wishes of the

terminal patient that will provide a positive and lasting memory for the family, particularly, the

children that will soon be left behind. Making Memories provides wonderful experiences that

give the family time together and help them cope with the eventual loss of the parent to cancer.

The memory created by the dying parent may be the very last thing they can do for their loved

ones and provides a memory they can hold in their heart for the rest of their lives. I can't

imagine that it fills the empty void left in your heart when you lose a loved one but it does

provide a special memory to cling to during the most difficult times. That is a good thing and a

wonderful service provided by Making Memories. However, at the time I didn't know what they

were about so in looking back, I probably wasn't as helpful as I could have been.

When Susie, an alert and committed volunteer for Making Memories, saw the story about

Annette on the news she immediately called the boys' father to tell him they would like to do

something for Annette and the boys. We really didn't understand how Making Memories

worked so after we discussed it, we declined their offer. There had been so much attention given

to Annette and the boys that things seemed to be getting out of control and we didn't want it to

escalate into becoming the proverbial three-ring circus.

Blessed with Cancer

The news announcement, in some variation between the newspapers and the television reports, focused the story on "these poor boys living with a single mom who is dying of breast cancer." There was some truth to it but it seemed more sensationalized and somewhat exaggerated. Anyone reading it could have taken it out of context and just thought the worst about the situation, which some did. Well-meaning reporters took up the banner and arranged for people to send money to a local bank to help the boys and their mother. Many businesses in the surrounding community wanted to help, as well, and some of them began doing their own thing to raise funds to help the boys. Some people assumed the boys would be left on their own after their mother's passing and have to either go into foster care or into some other state-funded program to provide for them. As the flood-tide of support continued it was impossible to stop the outpouring of everyone wanting to do something to help. The story was compelling and spoke to the good in so many people. It confirmed for me, in a very powerful and personal way, how caring and generous people are in this country. They all just wanted to help.

For a while, it was like a whirlwind of activities. The word got around, from business to business, from hair salon to hair salon. It seemed that so many people were talking about Annette and the boys. Unfortunately, like in the game "telephone", the story changes. There were a number of variations of the story going around, from Annette being healed, or she only had two weeks to live, or in one of the most bizarre variations, some thought it was actually me that was dying of breast cancer. How ironic was that? It got really crazy. The story went through so many mutations until, outside of Annette's immediate circle of family and friends, it wasn't clear what was really going on. What a wild time!

Because of all the outpouring of love and generous gifts, we had to open an account to establish a trust for the boys. In addition, one of their well-meaning relatives also opened up a

Blessed with Cancer

separate account at a different bank. This created some confusion as to where to make donations. Things were eventually sorted out and the good news was that the boys would be taken care of, another unexpected blessing.

Because my husband and I had declined the offer presented by Making Memories, Fran Hansen decided to go directly to Annette with the goal of granting her a special memory for her boys. Initially, I was not pleased that she had chosen to go around my husband and me to speak directly to Annette. In one sense, we believed we were protecting her, trying to make her life easier and less complicated. However, as I learned more about Making Memories and had a chance to get to know Fran and her daughter Anna, God changed my heart once again. This is when I decided that instead of being an obstacle to their good intentions I would help them in any way I could. After all, this was about Annette and the boys, not me.

Fran was the Founder of Making Memories and Anna was the President. I came to know them both as compassionate, caring and generous in their giving that I couldn't stand in the way. I also learned later that the two of them gave personally, as well as sacrificially, to grant memories for dying women. Now I am grateful for their persistence and recognize the purity of their intentions. God was bringing new blessings into our lives and that of Annette's. Who am I to get in the way of His divine plan and little did I know at the time what it would later mean to my own life.

Annette was so excited about the offer and readily said yes. She seemed to know instantly what she wanted to do for the boys and her request was for motorcycle dirt bikes. She instinctively knew this was something her boys would love and would be able to do together. It had been a difficult time for them and, although Annette would not be around, the boys could remember her every time they rode their dirt bikes. They would remember, "Mom did this for us." This is what I thought she was thinking and what I wanted to believe.

Making Memories immediately went to work doing what they do so well. Fran and Anna went about raising the funds to grant Annette's wish, including contacting appropriate businesses to ask their help to achieve the memory. One of the businesses contacted by Making Memories was a local motorcycle shop. As these things sometimes happen in God's divine plan, there was already a connection as the owner had gone to school with Annette many years earlier. When Making Memories shared Annette's story with him he naturally wanted to help. Therefore, Making Memories was able to purchase the motorized dirt bikes directly from the dealer who also made it possible for Making Memories to acquire the riding gear the boys would need to be safe, including helmets, gloves, goggles, shin protectors and chest protectors. I have to admit, it was kind of fun to tag along to the bike shop and watch the boys get outfitted with all the necessary equipment. It was like Christmas morning and you could see the total joy and excitement as this memory developed for the boys. To complete the package, a local auto dealership donated a bike trailer for transporting the bikes to the appropriate riding areas. Making Memories had created a wonderful experience for Annette and the boys and provided a memory the boys could always remember their mother by.

There was one final request from Annette but this time it was to her two boys. What she wanted from them was to do one final favor for her when she passed. Upon her death, her body was to be cremated. The boys would carry her ashes to their favorite riding area, Brown's Camp in Oregon, and spread her ashes on the mountain. Then, whenever they went riding, they would always know their mom was with them on the mountain. Timmy and Tyler gave their mother a special gift by doing just what she had asked of them. Mission accomplished.

Blessed with Cancer

This was my introduction to Making Memories and just the beginning of our relationship. I was so grateful to Fran and Anna for what they had done for Annette and the boys that I wanted to do whatever I could to help them. I made myself available to volunteer and, on a number of occasions, I became a spokesperson for the Making Memories foundation. Over the years they have given so many wonderful memories to the families of terminal breast cancer patients. It is and an honor to be associated with them in this way and Chanel and I stayed involved.

After Annette passed away Chanel and I took time each weak to volunteer at the Making Memories warehouse. Here they stored, sorted and organized hundreds of wedding dresses that had been donated to help raise funds for Making Memories. This unique program is called "Brides Against Breast Cancer," where the donated dresses are sold at special events across the country to raise money for Making Memories. The funds are used to help pay for many of the memories they create for dying women. What a wonderful cause and a great use of all those dresses that would otherwise hang in a closet or be stored in a box until they are forgotten or turned yellow beyond usefulness. Providing them to Making Memories is a great way to recycle these dresses and share with others.

We thought it was fun to work in the warehouse. One of our favorite assignments was to take donated dresses out of boxes, hang them up, size them and prepare them for sale or, when necessary, send them out to be cleaned. Occasionally, just for fun, we would try some of them on. Together Chanel and I handled hundreds of dresses. We would talk about the dresses and play games in our minds, trying to guess or create the fairy tale story behind each one. Of course, each story had to have a happy ending.

We never really knew where the dresses came from but we had fun thinking about it. We would ask things like, *"Was this dress ever worn?" What was the wedding like? Was it a simple wedding or an ultra elaborate affair, attended by kings and queens, royalty, presidents and heads of state?"* We had fun letting our minds run wild. We even created some possible scenarios, like the 'Runaway Bride,' or the bride left standing at the altar. Mostly, we thought about the wonderful life that was beginning for some lucky person and the joy she felt on her special day.

We also enjoyed some silent time just thinking about each dress, how it is designed or whether it was simple or ornate. Sometimes Chanel didn't say much and I suppose I had my times as well. Regardless, we were doing a good thing and giving back to Making Memories. They were present at a very difficult time in my life as well as Annette's. I even thought about how I wish she had survived and was there with me and Chanel preparing the dresses for some very lucky brides-to-be. What fun that would have been. I miss her.

Since that time Chanel and I have stayed involved in a number of ways with Making Memories. Once, Chanel had a chance to be a model for Making Memories and traveled with the future Miss Oregon, Katie Harman. Together they traveled around the state and to a few local preliminary pageants in preparation for the Miss Oregon Pageant. Katie was a wonderful influence on Chanel, as well as a good friend, and we were delighted when she was crowned Miss America in 2002. It was no surprise to us. She had such a radiance and awareness about her that you couldn't help but be encouraged and lifted up just being in her presence. We were blessed to be associated with this beautiful and caring individual and to be able to call her a friend.

I traveled to various Making Memories events to assist with their fundraisers. Where appropriate, I was also asked to be a spokesperson to share the story of Annette and how Making Memories makes a difference in the lives of so many breast cancer victims, most of whom do not

Blessed with Cancer

survive. After my own experience I was able to speak about the fight for survival as a person who was "better, not bitter." I also had the opportunity to go on a number of local television shows to represent Making Memories and at the same time share my on-going fight for survival. I was one of the lucky ones.

At this point I would do anything for Making Memories. I'd learned so much from them about commitment, sharing and giving back. An additional blessing is that Fran Hansen and I became close friends. She knew she could call on me anytime to share my story and Annette's with whatever audience she brought together for Making Memories fundraisers. Fran was also always available to me anytime, day or night, when I needed an understanding ear to hear my rollercoaster moods, frustrations, anger and fears. As incredibly busy as I know she is, with all the traveling she does to raise support for Making Memories, she always made time for me. I believe she was equally generous with so many other hurting women. I will forever be grateful to Fran for her love, understanding and genuine friendship.

Making Memories was now part of my life and I found myself trying to find other ways to help. One day, though I wasn't consciously thinking about Making Memories, a serendipitous moment presented a gem of an idea (pun intended). Having survived the first few rounds of treatment, surgery and recover for my own fight with breast cancer I was going through my jewelry box and found a diamond ring that I had not worn for a few years. I was no longer married to my third husband, the father of Annette's two sons, and I had put the ring away a few years back and forgot about it. Now as I was looking at it I realized I would most likely never wear it again. It occurred to me that I could donate it to Making Memories and maybe Fran could sell it to raise money for their program. I was not in a position to make a cash donation to

Blessed with Cancer

help Making Memories but I could give them the ring to help. I know it had value and I was sure they could use it in some way.

I was so excited that I called Fran right away and asked her to come by the store. I told her I had something and wanted to share an idea with her. When Fran came to the store I told her how much I appreciated all she and Anna had done for Annette and for me and that I wanted to do something to help. I shared the thoughts I'd had when going through my jewelry box and my decision to give her the ring. I suggested she could sell it to a jewelry store and use the money to help make a memory.

As I related my idea Fran's face lit up into this huge smile. At first she didn't say anything. She just beamed as she listened to me. When I finished, Fran explained that for the past few weeks she had been working on a similar idea but didn't know how to get started. When I offered my diamond ring it all came into perfect focus for her. She would use my ring to start a new fundraising program called "Diamonds for Dreams." In short, just like donating wedding dresses, people could donate their jewelry which would be sold to raise funds for Making Memories, creating another resource to make even more memories possible.

I certainly can't take credit for the idea that was already in progress but I couldn't be more excited about my diamond ring being the first piece of jewelry donated to this program. I'm also honored to know that my offer was the catalyst that helped Fran clarify this idea for a new program. I gave back and I couldn't be more delighted. Once again, as has happened so many times throughout this journey, I saw this as another "God thing." His hand was on the whole process. When we give in the true spirit of giving, which I hope I always do, with no promise of personal reward He blesses our efforts, no matter how small, to make great things happen.

Blessed with Cancer

Making Memories is used to make great things happen in the lives of so many families and providing special memories for a lifetime.   I thank God for programs like Making Memories.

Chapter 8 – The Unexpected Gift

"Nothing in this world is good or bad,
but thinking makes it so." William Shakespeare

It's been just about three months since Annette passed away. Looking back, it was a long

hard and emotionally-wrenching year and a half from the time she learned of her cancer to the

dark moment it took her life. Such an experience changes us all. It's interesting how "life

events", and they happen to all of us, can completely change the direction of a story. These

events are not so unlike paradigm shifts that take place in movies and drive the plot in a whole

new direction. Something is revealed somewhere in the storyline that gives us an "ah-ha"

moment, a discovery of new information and creates a situation that makes it necessary for the

hero or heroine to respond differently to take different steps to achieve the sometimes happy

ending. A friend of mine tells me there are usually two paradigms in a movie story. The first is

about 30 minutes into the movie and the second is usually about an hour later, with twenty to

thirty minutes to resolve the challenge leading to the climax event and a different outcome as a

result of the new information. I believe that in life we experience paradigm shifts all the time.

It would be nice if life was more predictable but as we experience it we respond to the changes

as best we can. I think we have all been told at one time or another that it isn't what happens to

us that determines our success or failure but how we handle what happens. Boy, isn't that the

truth. Thank God there is Someone who cares for us and is always there for us. This is one of

the truths I've learned through these experiences. When we are going through the darkest times

of our lives we may not believe God is here let alone believe that He even exists. But, regardless

of whether or not we believe in Him, He always believes in us. The Bible says that He promises

Blessed with Cancer

He will be with us always. What a great reassurance. This promise gives us hope and hope gives us a reason to go on.

Since Annette's passing my husband and I were no longer together. In fact, we were now divorced and I was raising the two boys, Timmy and Tyler, as well as my daughter, Chanel. We were no longer together for a number of reasons but I realized our marriage was in trouble long before Annette died. When Annette and I took our "bonding" trip to Bend the relationship between my husband and me was already terminally strained and we headed toward separation. It wasn't just the passing of Annette but other "life events" as well. Things were tough all around but for my husband, they were too much to handle and it seemed to affect him the most. I tried to understand and consoled myself by remembering that Annette had been his first wife and the mother of their two boys. This is the only part of my life that will remain private and isn't really relevant except to say that he'd lost his business and experienced a nervous breakdown. In addition his own father had also passed away not too long before and things didn't get better for him. He was different toward the family and the boys in particular, began to resent him. Our marriage ended but life went on.

I was a single mother raising three children, home-schooling and spending as much time with them as possible. I enjoyed spending time with them in this way and believed it to be important for all our healing but realized that I needed to do something to generate the income necessary for us to live. It didn't help when I had an accident and had to have back surgery. I should have known better, being as small as I am, but there was some work that needed to be done and I couldn't wait any longer for help. I was confident it would be okay so I spent a day lifting and carrying bark dust to put in the plant areas around my business. This was apparently the final straw, or bark chip, for my back because, before the day was done, the work had herniated a disk in my lower back. I can't blame it all on the bark dust and the heavy lifting, though.

For years I had carried my daughter Chanel around on my hip which I think may have already started the damage in my back. My friends even told me I shouldn't do it, that it was probably not good for me. At the time I weighed just over one hundred pounds, a hundred and one to be exact. Chanel was 8 years old and she weighed about 80 pounds. It was a bad idea but I enjoyed this closeness with my daughter and I was to pay the price. My friends were right. Chanel's weight, along with lifting loads of bark dust that day was just too much and it put me in the hospital. Earlier I told you about paradigm shifts in my story. Well, this was one of those. God was about to provide another blessing.

I can't say that my father and I didn't have a relationship because that would not be the truth. However, on most occasions, it was strained to say the least. In fairness to my dad, I hadn't always made the best decisions in my life and my choice of men turned out to be the worst. This really troubled my dad and I now realize that it was a constant concern and frustration for him. Don't get me wrong, it wasn't what you might be thinking. A better description would be that I was too naïve and trusting and believed the things men told me. I'm sure this was somewhat a result of how I was raised and lack of belief in my own personal worth. I was always trying to fill a void in my life, wanting to marry a man, have a baby and a family. . That's the way I thought it should be. I would later learn that I had what is now referred to as the "Cinderella Syndrome." In short, I always wanted to be swept off my feet by a handsome prince and be carried away on his white horse to live happily ever after. It didn't work that way and I was left vulnerable by believing that it could. While growing up, I was treated differently in my house by both my father and my two brothers. More often than I can really recall, my dad would make

Blessed with Cancer

comments to me which communicated that I would never amount to much. He seemed to favor my brothers and I felt that I was less than equal to them. Young as I was, it hurt and I never understood why he would say those things. I just accepted that it was the way it would be. Many times I longed to hear words of encouragement and for him to tell me that I was going to be okay.

One day, while I was still in the hospital recovering from my back surgery, I was trying to get in touch with my ex-husband to help with the kids but was unable to reach him. I didn't know where he was but thought I would be able to get him on his cell phone. For some reason he had turned it off, something he rarely did. I thought, "What kind of a jerk would turn off his phone at a time like this?" I needed his help and had nowhere else to turn. I was so frustrated I even considered calling my dad but couldn't bring myself to do it. I found out later that one of the nurses looked on the emergency contact list that I filled out earlier and she called my dad to tell him what was going on. Most of that day I was in tears and not totally all together but I couldn't call my father and ask for help. He lived all the way up in Seattle, Washington, which seemed so far away. However I think the nurse believed I needed someone, that I needed my daddy, so she made the call. I was in and out of sleep all day. I felt no pain but I was alone and sleeping was a welcome relief.

Later that day I woke up, somewhat still in a haze, and I realized that someone was stroking my hair. It was such a comforting feeling. I was enjoying it so much I felt like I was still in a dream and not really awake. I didn't want to wake up. The touch of a person's hand, especially the stroking of your hair, is such a warm, loving feeling and I wanted to enjoy the moment. As I lay there my curiosity got the best of me and I realized it wasn't a dream. Someone really was stroking my hair. Whoever they were, they cared enough to give me this gift of human touch.

Blessed with Cancer

As I tried to clear my head to look up at the angel treating me in this special way, I realized it was my father. I must have been asleep for a long time because my dad had to drive all the way down from Seattle to be with me. He was there for me and was stroking my hair in such a loving way that my heart swelled with the warmth of this special blessing. I tried to talk but wasn't very coherent. I wanted to express how much it meant to me to wake up and see him there. The fact that he was there, though, stroking my hair was comfort enough.

Then he did something totally unexpected, which meant the whole world to me. He leaned down, close to my face, spoke to me in a soft whisper and said, "Honey, everything is going to be alright. It's tough right now but you'll get through this." Wow! Was this my father talking? Then he went even further to show how much he loved me. Everyone knew that I was going to be in bed for the next thirty days or so during my recovery. He told me that while I was in bed, "I want you to spend a lot of your time thinking about a business, something that you really want to do. Decide what your business will look like and map it out in every detail. Close your eyes and visualize everything you can about your new business. When you are up on your feet again, and well enough, I am going to help you start that new business."

I didn't know what to say. This was almost too much for me to comprehend. I don't recall if I'd ever before been at such a loss for words, but I was. My only explanation now is that I was probably in some stage of shock. Maybe it was the morphine that made me so slow to respond or maybe I was just caught up in taking it all in. I remember it was more than I had ever expected and something I had not even imagined. The fact that my dad was really there sitting by my bed, caressing my head and giving his loving support made me realize it was all true. I accepted this as all a part of a bigger plan. His offer was precisely the reassurance that I needed to hear and it was beyond my understanding that it came from my dad. I could no longer contain the tears that welled up in my eyes or the warmth that consumed my heart or the love I felt for this man. It was love like I'd never experienced before. I don't know what changed but God gave me exactly what I needed at the precise moment in my life when I needed it. That really isn't surprising at all when it comes to our wonderful God. As we all eventually learn, these life-events always happen in God's timing. I believe He does these things to show He cares but many times in a way that we then know it was God making it happen. At the end of the day, I finally believed that everything was going to be alright.

Chapter 9 – The Bird Whistle

*"Opportunity often comes in the form of misfortune
or temporary defeat."* Napoleon Hill

Between my time in the hospital and my time recovering at home I was in bed for about 30 days. However, as my dad had told me to do I spent a lot of my awake time thinking about what type of business I would like to have. That took some thinking and some real soul-searching. I didn't know right away for sure what it would be. It needed to be something to which I would really want to devote all my time and effort. It had to be more than a casual interest and more like something that would create in me a real passion for the products or services. It also had to be a business where I could really relate to my customers and make them my friends, while at the same time meeting their specific needs through my store. Being a single mom with a daughter and two boys to raise I had to come up with something that I could handle but also something that would allow me to stay connected to my children. It really helped me to focus when I realized that I wanted a place where my kids could come to help out and get involved in the business if they wanted to. It would be a great learning experience for all of us while giving us time together as a family.

I'd heard many stories of starting a new business and how much time and effort it required to be successful. I ran a lot of questions through my mind. What kind of a business would be unique enough to create a demand for it? What kind of products or services would I have in my store and would it be successful enough to provide for our financial needs. I also wanted a special name that would set my store apart from all others. Finally it came to me. I would open up a pet store called Exclusive Pet Food. This is perfect. The kids would love it, especially with all the animals, and customers with their pets. This is going to be the greatest experience and a real healing place. That last point, although it was the final selling point, would be the "key" residual benefit to everything we did there. The pet store would be a refuge for me and my children, not only to provide for our needs but a place to help us heal from all that we had been through over the past couple of years. I couldn't wait to get started.

As soon as I was able to get up and walk I immediately went out and applied for a business license. Initially, because of the back surgery, any effort to get up and move around was difficult. The doctor and nurses told me things would be this way but, in time, my pain would subside and my life would get better. For sure, the pain was significant and mostly constant. However, I was motivated. I was excited. I could tolerate the pain, knowing it would become less and less as I continued to exercise my muscles and joints. Thirty-plus days is a long time to spend on your back in bed and it was time to get on with my life. I had work to do and children to support. Once I received my business license I really felt that my dream was going to happen. My excitement and enthusiasm grew as the reality of owning my own store became clearer. My Exclusive Pet Food store was about to become a reality.

Now that I had decided what kind of a store it would be and what would be my "niche", I began to visualize what it would look like. With that in mind I made numerous trips to the local Goodwill Thrift Store to find what I would need to give my pet food store its own unique personality....its own special ambiance. Goodwill stores always seem to have an interesting variety of beautiful and unique knick-knacks and other items that are perfect for decorating. I looked for ceramic pieces and figurines, picture frames or anything that had animals on it. I was especially drawn to things with dogs, cats and birds on them. I didn't find everything I wanted in one trip but Goodwill seems to have a consistent stream of new product arriving all the time and

Blessed with Cancer

it was only a matter of time before I found everything I needed. I found it pretty amazing what people would give away. I'd heard someone say one time that "one person's trash is another person's treasure." I can believe that now. I experienced it first hand and the treasures I was finding would make the perfect décor for my new venture. This would make the store unique and it would be a fun place for me, my children and all of our customers.

I opened the store shortly after the boy's mom passed away. This turned out to be a wonderful idea, I must say. At that time it was the greatest place in the world for my whole family. The store was everything I hoped it would be and was a place to which the kids and I could retreat. It proved to be a miraculous healing place for all of us. The kids got to run the cash register, throw freight, mark-price merchandise and move things around as needed. They were all such a great help and the boys, especially, took care of some of the heavier jobs of loading and unloading the larger bags of pet food and similar "manly" chores. They also got to help, or should I really say "play", with the interesting new toys for cats and dogs. They especially looked forward to the customers as they came in with their numerous varieties of pets. The store brought in big dogs and little dogs; one-pound dogs you could hold, like teacup poodles and yorkies, and big dogs I wanted to hold but sometimes they weighed more than me or the kids. We saw Rotteweilers, a big black Newfoundland and, gosh, even a cute, but huge, Newfoundland puppy. There were cute kittens and cats, at least until a dog came in. Then pandemonium broke and none of them were cute anymore. The cats came in all sizes, shapes and colors, including bald cats, fat cats, no-tail cats and more. The activities of the store provided a constant and ever-changing population of four and two-legged creatures which kept the kids always intrigued and pre-occupied. What a wonderful and constant smorgasbord of blessings to experience every day.

Blessed with Cancer

Thank goodness for all the craziness and busyness around me, especially with the demands of my store. It was a marvelous distraction for all of us and provided a different focus in our lives following the death of my friend, and the boys' mother, Annette. It was during this time that I learned I had breast cancer and began the series of four surgeries and numerous treatments to save my life. This was my "lost summer" because it was so full of activity and I was in and out of the hospital. I was never able to enjoy a relaxed season as other summers had been in the past.

After every surgery, the moment I was well enough I returned to my store to work and maintain my business. In all honesty, I never was "well-enough" to go back to work but I knew I had to for a number of reasons. I do believe this gave me purpose, served as a distraction and, indeed, helped me along the way. My store was truly a place of healing with many of the animals who brought their owners in to see how I was doing.

Little blessings can come to us in some of the most unlikely ways and at the most unexpected times. We may not see them right away but they eventually make themselves known. It is not so unusual but, like many children, my daughter, Chanel, wanted a bird. Well, actually, she really wanted a cat or a dog, but I could barely take care of myself and the children. Adding the additional responsibility of a dog or a cat would have just been too much for me. My kids may have made an effort to say they would take care of it but it doesn't always work out that way and the parent, me, ends up having one more live creature for which to be responsible. Bringing a pet into the home isn't like ordering a pizza. They need to be cared for, fed, relieved and treated like one of the family. They literally become part of the family and find their place in the family unit. For me, it would be just one more responsibility on top of everything else I was trying to do. Maybe we could get a pet at another time.

Blessed with Cancer

However, Chanel was not going to give up on her desire to have a pet of her own. After all, her mom owned a pet store. She came to me with what I thought was a reasonable alternative, or compromise, and I agreed. She decided she would be satisfied with a bird and agreed that she would be fully responsible for taking care of it and that it wouldn't be a burden to her mother. She was so convincing that I said "yes" and we sat down to discuss the key considerations of choosing the right bird to join our family. If Chanel was going to have her own pet, just the right bird, she was going to have to do her homework on this subject. Together we decided she should go online and search/research some choices in birds. She was to find out what she could about Parakeets, Cockatiels and Cockatoos. Here's what she learned.

Chanel decided right away that a Cockatoo would be too big, requiring a lot more attention than we may be able to give it. Besides, they can bite harder. She also felt that a Parakeet would be too small and perhaps too fragile to be handled as much as she would like to. She finally decided that a Cockatiel would be just right. It would be much easier to take care of in a bird cage. Her next step, at my suggestion, was to write a letter to the Bird Rescue and see if she could find a Cockatiel that was in need of a home. After a short period of checking around, she actually found one. It sounded perfect and the Cockatiel was waiting at the shelter for someone to choose him. The bird was originally owned by a 6-year-old little girl who had received it as a gift. The bird ended up at the rescue shelter because it had been mistreated. I don't know all the details of the bird's story but I knew Chanel wanted him and that she would take very good care of the bird. I was so proud of how Chanel went about applying for her pet. Not only did she fill out the appropriate application to be considered to receive the Cockatiel, she also provided a bio of herself and detailed her responsibilities at the pet store. Her extra effort was successful and she was rewarded by being chosen out of twelve other applicants to receive the bird. Chanel was now the proud new owner of a beautiful grey and white Cockatiel, rescued from the shelter. The day I arrived home from the hospital we received a call from a lady ready to deliver Chanel's new pet bird. What perfect timing! You might even say it was by Divine appointment. As the Bible reminds us, God's eye is even on the little sparrow. I think that also includes the Cockatiel.

Chanel's attention was now diverted to her new friend, Cinder. Chanel and Cinder only had a few days in which to get to know each other before school started. After a great summer vacation working in the pet store and getting to know her new feathered friend, Chanel was really dreading getting back into the routine of school. I am sure you remember how it was for you or even your child. What Chanel really dreaded was going into the sixth grade, the first year of junior high school in our district, making new friends, learning new routines and just trying to fit in. For Chanel it was, in her words, "really scary!" Also, all of her friends were going to different schools. I wasn't yet physically ready to drive, at least for a week, so a friend of mine would pick up Chanel and take her to school for me. I really had some wonderfully caring and supportive friends who helped me through this difficult period, including manning the store in my absence. I tried to be encouraging by saying something that Chanel really understood would have meaning for the both of us. *"Chanel, be brave at your first day of Junior High School,"* I said, *"and I will be brave on my first day to look at the new me."* Off to school she went, momentarily looking back to encourage me with her smile.

I remember the day. It was quiet, warm and sunny and it was time. I'd made an agreement with Chanel and it was time for me to remove the bandages on my chest and see what remained after six major surgeries to remove my breast cancer. As I had done so many times before, I walked into the bathroom to take off my shirt and stood in front of the full length mirror. Then I removed the bandages. In my heart and soul, even before I looked, I felt such a relief. The first thought that ran through my head was the assurance by the doctor that my cancer was gone. Now it was time to see the toll it had taken. I had to focus on removing my bandages. Was I ready to take this step? No, but I couldn't stay covered up forever. Denial is a pretty natural human defense mechanism when we aren't ready to face the truth. I just didn't know if I was quite ready to see the new me. How could I be? How do you prepare for an unveiling such as this? In one way, I was in constant praise and gratitude for the fact that I was alive. My cancer was gone and I get to see my daughter grow into a young lady and then into a woman. The promise of this gift was more important to me than anything else. I was only putting off the inevitable. I'd made an agreement with Chanel. Now it was time to take the step, ready or not.

I removed the bandages and it was very different to see nothing on my chest except scars of various sizes. In addition, there were two very prominent long scars, one on each side, right where my breasts used to be. I stared for awhile, really studying each scar and the accompanying stitch marks. I don't recall how long I stood there but it probably wasn't as long as I imagined. I covered up, happy the cancer was gone but kind of blah, numb, not really sure how I should feel. I was glad to be alive while at the same time feeling some level of depression and disappointment.

I was relatively young at 40 years of age, with so much future in front of me, but my chest looked like an amputated mess. Just at that moment when I was feeling down, maybe the lowest I'd experienced in a while, Cinder started to whistle. It may have been my imagination but it sounded almost like a bugler trumpeting the arrival of royalty. Tumptadadum…..tumptadadum.. (at least, that is what I heard in my head). Prior to this Cinder had not made one peep. It was all so strange and so unexpected, I started to laugh. I couldn't help myself. My momentary "pity party" was over. Through Cinder, God reminded me that He was always with me. In the past years, I knew that I would embrace whatever I was going through and would do whatever it took to get through it. I was alive and was once again reminded of that reality through the music of Cinder's voice. But, Cinder wasn't done. My spirit was already lifting and my soul was on the rise. What he did next was so unexpected it made me burst out in uncontrollable laughter. Cinder came out with a perfect rendition of a wolf's whistle, "fweeeeeefwuuuuuu", something you might expect from a construction worker that sees a beautiful girl walk by and can't contain his admiration. I laughed so hard it was a good thing I was in the bathroom, if you know what I mean. I almost peed my pants. I can only believe that God had brought Cinder into my life and put him into my home just for this moment. Wow! I couldn't wait for Chanel to get home so I could tell her the story. It was too good not to be shared. In an instant, Cinder endeared himself to me forever.

When I wasn't at the store, I spent a lot of time at home with Cinder while Chanel was at school. Sometimes, it seemed like the only the conversations I had during the day were with him and I'll admit, the conversations were pretty one-sided. I spoke my mind, shared my concerns and did a lot of thinking "out loud." He agreed with me by including an occasional encouraging chirp. Cinder was a great listener. I would share my pains, my fears, my hopes and my dreams and he would sit there patiently taking it all in. Just to show me he was interested, he would cock his head to one side or the other, back and forth, as if contemplating everything I had to say. And, on occasion, his head would go up and down, as if he was agreeing with me or showing his approval. I loved it. I would never have imagined it but this small relationship with one of Gods tiny winged creatures was so good for me. It turned out to be a very special blessing and a wonderful time of healing. God knew what I needed and sent his messenger, another angel, into my life just at the right time with just the right message. In my heart, this was a message of reassurance that told me that I am going to be fine. My life is going to be great, and whole again. Just like the sparrow in the song, God has his ever-caring eye on little ol' me. I couldn't ask for more!

Chapter 10 – The Dress

"The state of your life is nothing more than a reflection of your state of mind." Wayne Dyer

Out of the blue, I got a call from my good friend, Kim. She was always fun, impulsive and full of surprises. Kim called and asked me if I wanted to go with her to Las Vegas. Actually, it was more like, "Let's go to Las Vegas. It would really be fun." I said, "Las Vegas, as in Las Vegas, Nevada?" Her call was either providential or just a stroke of superb timing. Regardless, it was a serendipitous call at the very least. During that period in my life I was transitioning my work from inside an office to work in outside sales. This was a personally unwanted change in my job assignment and required some adjustments on my part. For some time now it had been a difficult, demanding load as I learned the ins and outs of "hitting the streets" and making the calls. As I was learning, I discovered I had some natural abilities in this area. I was finally gaining the skills I needed to be successful but, it was still a personal challenge. I had to work at it. When Kim called, it came just at the right time. I needed a few days off although I wasn't thinking that I actually had time to do it. In reality, I needed to get away to somewhere else, have no responsibilities and just rest, enjoy and pamper myself. Las Vegas sure fit that bill.

Kim usually goes to Las Vegas alone but this time, for some reason, she decided to call me. I'm just one of Kim's many friends but she really knew how to make me feel special. Because of the kind of person she is, I'm confident that she probably makes all her friends feel the same way. I met Kim about five years earlier when she was referred to me by a mutual friend. We seemed to have so much in common and we clicked right away. One specific thing that we had in common, which brought us even closer, was that her mother had breast cancer just a few years

Blessed with Cancer

before. Some people consider me a major connector. I don't know how true that is but I do like to introduce people and organizations that have common interests or where there can be some synergy. By this, I mean that people or organizations can work together for the common good of everyone in the relationship. Each has something to bring to the table that benefits the other. It is all about joining efforts and resources to achieve success. Because I like to connect people, I introduced Kim to Making Memories Breast Cancer Foundation. I thought it would be a good fit and that Kim could help. Together we formed a fundraising march which was quite successful. Through the process we became good friends.

Kim and I would get together once a month but would talk on the phone almost every day. She is a good friend, really cares for me and always looks out for my best interests as she does for so many other people. Kim is a very strong personality. Over the years, when I've needed her, she has been there to be my friend and share my life. In one sense we are almost like twin sisters, except I am a brunette and she is a blonde. You can believe that created some opportunities to joke and kid about "blondes" over the years. Also, we wear the same size and that is pretty unusual considering how tiny I am.

It was a spur-of-the-moment idea ..... spontaneous. Kim went to Las Vegas the day before me. I had to work it out to get time off from work but I was able to do that with relative ease. A friend took me to the airport and I took my favorite carrier, Alaska Airlines.

I knew it would be a pretty quick flight from Portland, Oregon, to Las Vegas and I was really looking forward to getting there. Living in the Pacific Northwest has its advantages. When you are flying out of Portland, depending on where in the plane you are seated, you get a beautiful view of the incredible, snow-capped Mount Hood. Its grandeur always gives me a moment of pause and I reflect on God's goodness represented by the beauty that surrounds us. The

98

mountain is tremendous. There is also very little that can compare to the trees, the rivers, lakes, waterfalls and mountains that represent the Northwest. Unless you've seen it first hand, or experienced it, it's hard to comprehend. It is just so wonderful here.

If you are lucky enough to be sitting on the left side of the plane as it travels south, you'll also get to see a number of other great Oregon mountains. And, if you're really lucky, the pilot will get your attention and alert you to a glimpse of beautiful, crystal clear, Crater Lake. There is nothing more breathtaking than this unique body of water and its pristine, reflective, glass-like surface. It's even more spectacular during the winter when the surrounding mountains are covered in snow. What a great way to enjoy the flight, by losing yourself in the snapshots of nature's beauty.

I was really looking forward to getting to Las Vegas and seeing my friend. Although Kim is one of my favorite people, we don't have the opportunity to get together like this very often. When we do it is absolutely wonderful. She is such a great friend, and we have so much fun. It may be one of those spontaneous combustion moments when she and I get together. There is something crazy and explosive about our relationship but in a fun, party-like way.

Kim had arranged to have a car meet me when I arrived to take me to the hotel. We were staying at The Wynn Hotel which is owned by Stephen Wynn who also owns the Hotel Bellagio. You know .... the one with the big fountain that puts on a spectacular water spray show. When I got to the hotel, the car delivered me to the special VIP entrance. Wow! What a special treat. I felt like I had just won a huge pageant and was being treated like royalty. Since I was once again caught up in the moment, I guess I could have said that I felt like I had just won an Oscar at the very prestigious Academy Awards. As the car pulled up to the VIP entrance, my beautiful and gorgeous friend, Kim, was standing outside waiting to greet me. After our uncontrollable

Blessed with Cancer

display of excitement, giggling, hellos, et al, Kim escorted me to our suite so I could get settled in before dinner. We were like college roommates, getting together for the first time many years after graduating and going off to pursue our separate careers. It was so great to see her.

We went to dinner at a beautiful restaurant in the hotel. Unfortunately, I was on a "fast" for a ministry in which I was involved, called Healing Streams. This was the last week of a seven-week commitment preparing for an upcoming Bible retreat. Since I was half-way through the week of fasting I just couldn't bring myself to break the "fast", not even for Las Vegas. It was too important and I'd come a long way to get to this point so I didn't order what you might consider a nice restaurant meal. All I had was some fresh, sourdough bread dipped in oil and balsamic dressing.

After dinner we went out into the casino to enjoy a few of the games. We played some Roulette but it wasn't my most successful experience so I didn't stay there very long. We went off to the slots and played the Mermaid penny machines for a little while. Even that didn't go so well so we didn't spend too much time there, either. For us, it wasn't so much about winning, although that makes it much better, but it was about being together and having fun.

I think the weeks of work and training finally caught up with me. I realized that I was more in need of rest and relaxation so we made it a short night. I was also hungry so maybe the "fast" was taking its toll as well. However, the fast would be over in the morning. Then it would be every woman for herself. "Watch out buffet, I'll be back."

Friday was a "SPA" day which was a real treat and something I always look forward to. We went to the pool to lie in the sun. It was so nice to have no responsibilities and to just be free to relax. I had my sunglasses and a good book, "Conversations with God." Another girlfriend of mine had given it to me. She felt it was a good time for me to read a book that made me think. Actually, I think all the time but in this case she was referring to a time of introspection…looking inside myself.

I was enjoying the book when I became aware of some guys who were checking us out. I was wearing sunglasses so I was able to observe what they were doing without them really knowing it. At first I tried to ignore them and stay focused on my book. However, after a while it actually became comical. They were obviously trying to work their way over to where we were so they could start a conversation. Could they be any more obvious? It struck me particularly funny because it could have been a segment on the television program called Animal Planet, titled something like "The Mating Habits of the North American Homosapiens." Or it could have even been a new realty TV game show. Anyway, they finally made their way over and started a conversation with us, at least for a short while.

Mostly, we talked about a new video poker game using a touch screen. It was fun for awhile, but we really weren't interested in starting relationships with these strangers, especially one over a weekend in Las Vegas. You know…"what happens in Vegas stays in Vegas." Well, not for these chicks. It was flattering but we only had a few days and there were things we wanted to do. So, we ditched them and went off to the casinos to try out the new game.

We met up with a couple of friends from Portland who were also there for the weekend. We did some gambling, played games, had some drinks and enjoyed a water feature show. Beautifully choreographed water jets danced to the music while colored lighting enhanced the mood of the performance. The special effects, creative illusions and some robotic elements worked together to mesmerize and entertain the audience. What a magical place and there are so many places to go in Las Vegas to see great shows, from singers and dancers to magicians and comedians. The options for good, clean entertainment are unlimited. Just seeing the sights and

Blessed with Cancer

the various casinos could keep you entertained for days, let alone hours. Wow. What great fun. Once again we were good girls and didn't stay out very late. Sleep, relaxation and no set schedule was a perfect agenda for me.

The next morning started slow. Both Kim and I slept in until sometime after ten o'clock. That is unusual for me because I am always up and going around six in the morning. However, today I had nothing I had to rush off to do and the bed was so warm and comfortable that I wanted to enjoy it to its fullest.

We decided to have breakfast in the room and take our time getting started. I read the newspaper while I ate and made a few phone calls. I was enjoying the moment…no stress and no schedule…just a totally relaxing experience with a good friend. Kim was great and she wasn't pushing to drive an agenda, either. We were taking full advantage of not having any obligations except to ourselves. I think everyone should give themselves this special gift a few times a year. It doesn't have to be about going to Las Vegas, or some other exotic location, but just taking some time for you. Life is so much better when we do that.

The day was pretty much a repeat of yesterday except that Kim went off to the spa to spend more time being pampered and I went back to the swimming pool. The sun was warm and I wanted to keep working on a tan. I have the right kind of skin that allows me to get a nice tan relatively quickly and I wanted to look like I'd been somewhere when I got home. And, I still had my book. I lost myself in the pages for a few hours, sometimes just closing my eyes to think about what I was reading. I think I even nodded off a couple of times and that was okay.

Some people say Las Vegas is the place to cut loose, let your inhibitions go and just have a wild and crazy, out-of-control time. You can drink, gamble, go to a show or two, wear anything you want, meet guys and party throughout the night, day after day. That's what some people do

Blessed with Cancer

but for me and Kim, we weren't interested in those kinds of distractions. We didn't have that kind of time to waste. Our agenda entailed nails, the ones on your fingers and toes, hair, facials, full-body massage, sauna, whirlpool, steam room, lay by the pool, lunch, naps, refresh and having our make-up done. In short….pamper, pamper and more pamper, all the things a woman should do to feel like a woman. Actually, we all know there is so much more to being a woman than that but there are times when this is exactly what is called for. This was one of those times. Later that afternoon I went back to the room to relax some more and wait for Kim.

Our plans for that evening were to go out on the town. It was going to be a little more special than the other nights. I had even brought a really cute little sun dress with spaghetti straps. It was a cream and black dress with a plunging neckline. *"A plunging neckline?!"* What was I thinking? I was initially feeling bold and adventurous but when it came time to start getting ready I got cold feet. In short, I was becoming very self-conscious and uncomfortable. The reality of my surgery slammed to the forefront of my mind, reminding me of what I had gone through, how the look of my chest had changed so dramatically and how I was left with these large, exaggerated scars. The thought was creating a sense of panic. So many things were running through my mind. If I wear this dress, the plunging neckline will reveal the numerous scars crossing my chest. I wasn't ready for that.

I was afraid that everyone would see them and focus on how they looked. How would the people react? Would they even notice? Of course they would. These are no small scars. These are painful reminders of a very difficult time in my life. They are so big and ugly I was sure people were bound to notice them. They would probably think "Why doesn't she cover those things up? What is she trying to prove?" This is what was going through my mind. I was thinking of every possible reason to let myself off the hook and not wear the dress.

Blessed with Cancer

Kim saw the dress I was trying on and said "Linda, you look beautiful in that dress. You have got to wear it." I blurted out, *"Oh no, I don't think so."* She wouldn't give up and said, "But you look fabulous!" I was still fighting the urge to chicken out and kept running the same self-defeating thought through my head. Women don't go out showing these kinds of scars on their chests. They don't want people to know, probably for the same self-conscious reasons I didn't want people to know. I was different...I wasn't normal. I was no longer whole. The thought of not being whole really hurt and it hurt deep down inside my soul. Would a man ever look at me the same? I didn't think so. In our society today, especially in a place like Las Vegas, there is a huge emphasis on a woman having perfect breasts. Many women go to so much trouble to have them made perfect. In the case of women like me, when I've had to have six major surgeries to save my life and in the painful process had my most visible and symbolic female parts taken away, I didn't feel very good about myself. I didn't feel very woman-like. During some of my lower moments I felt like I was a real "freak" and wondered if I would ever be accepted as a whole woman again. I know it was all in my mind but it was very real.

Fortunately, my friend was being a real friend and wouldn't let me get away with that or anything that resembled a pity party. Kim, a beautiful woman herself, continued to encourage me by telling me how beautiful I was and how well that dress fit me. I really wanted to wear it but had gotten myself so worked up I just didn't feel I could. I was so afraid that if I went out in this dress my scars would be "spot-lighted" everywhere I went. Would people notice them and try to get a better look, without staring or getting caught? What assumptions would they make?

This was about overcoming fears and doubts. Why was I having a problem with it? There are men and women out there who are missing limbs. Some have lost one or both legs. Others have lost arms or hands, yet they still go out in public. They have learned to cope. They go out

Blessed with Cancer

and enjoy life. They may be on crutches, in a wheelchair or have learned to work with a variety of prostheses. It is accepted. It has become more common and people are more accepting of seeing these extraordinary people functioning in society. In many cases they are even admired for their courage and effort to be among the "normal." So, why was I having such a difficult time? Maybe it was stage fright. I was afraid that I would be on stage and all eyes would be focused on me and my scars.

Finally, I took a deep breath and said okay. Staring in the mirror for the umpteenth time I made one final application of make-up and powder to the scarred areas, turned around, smiled at Kim and headed out the door. Once the door closed behind us there was no turning back. We walked down the hallway, into the elevators and then out of the elevators onto the main floor of the casino. Kim was a constant encouragement, not just by what she said but by the fact that she acted normal and talked to me like all of this was perfectly normal. Talking all the while heading to the restaurant for dinner, we maneuvered our way through the other guests and by more people sitting at the slot machines and roulette tables. I felt like I wanted to cover up or crawl under the tables. Occasionally, Kim would say, "Are you okay?", and I would nod my head. We kept going. Surprisingly enough, no one looked at me like I was a freak. I don't think they even noticed my scars. A couple of times, although I tried not to make eye contact with anyone, I experienced a pleasant smile from a stranger, a man, as if to say "Hi, you're gorgeous." As the evening went on I reflected on Kim's question earlier when she asked if I was okay. It became clearer for me that yes, I am OKAY. I am blessed and more than okay. Wow, life or death? I am alive and so blessed with life.

Let me tell you a little secret about myself. The truth is, I was pretty shy as a child, and was never very confident growing up. Even as a young woman and married, I couldn't step out and do things on my own. Until I went through all this cancer stuff and made the decision to fight

for my life, I pretty much just went along with whatever happened. Breast cancer changed all

that and girl, did I grow up. It all seems like just a memory now but it gave me a whole new

perspective about me and life and all it has to offer.

Sometimes, in fact, too many times we put things in our head and imagine the worst. I know

you understand what I am talking about. You have probably heard the phrase, "**FEAR** stands for

False **E**vidence **A**ppearing **R**eal." That is so true. We create things in our mind based on

whatever fears we have and exaggerate the feeling, sometimes to the point of not taking action.

Our self-talk is more damaging to our own success than anything anyone else could say or do.

We do it to ourselves. Another old adage that is also so true is that the only thing we need to fear

is fear itself. Well, I'm not afraid anymore. If Kim, my friend, and I'm re-emphasizing that she

is my friend because I am so grateful for her intervention at this point....... but if Kim hadn't

bolstered my confidence and helped me step out by encouraging me to wear the dress, I probably

would not have worn such a dress, even to this day. I'd have kept my scars concealed, and

hidden from view. Wearing the dress, the healing experience that it brought and the emboldened

confidence it gave me, took my life to a new level of acceptance and enjoyment. Kim's

encouragement was the blessing I needed just at the time when I needed it. It was a huge step in

my healing process, once again, confirming that God's timing is always best. That weekend in

Las Vegas was one more blessing that made me realize that life is good and, life is worth living,

and for sure, life is worth fighting for. I am so glad I did and I am so grateful for my friends.

My confidence was growing. You see, with the encouragement of my friend I made a

decision. I could try and hide behind anything and everything and understandably create the

excuses that would justify my hiding. Instead, I chose to wear this beautiful dress and walk with

Blessed with Cancer

my head high and my battle scars exposed. As one of my other friends put it, these are my medals for surviving a horrible disease, one that attempted to take my life. I took a deep breath and through this simple walk of faith, announced: *"It's me. I'm alive and I'm beautiful, scars and all."* The evening was wonderful and it wasn't long before I'd forgotten all about my scars. I was playing and dancing and just enjoying the company of Kim and my other friends, celebrating life and Las Vegas. We can always take confidence in knowing that no matter what others may think, whatever fears we may create in our minds, whatever challenges life may bring our way, we can overcome them. If we are open to the possibilities and believe that good things can happen, I believe they will. They did for me that night and I've never looked back.

Chapter 11 – Who Is Kay Woods?

"For I know the plans I have for you, says the Lord. Plans to prosper and not harm you. Plans to give you hope and a future.   Jeremiah 29:11

"Who is Kay Woods?" Now that is an interesting question. For more than half of my life, I didn't know. When I finally found out so many things started to make sense. However, I'm kinda getting ahead of myself. I'll have to tell you about her in a little bit and how I came to find out who she is. But right now I need to share something else with you. It's a bit personal, but important. It's not easy but it is easier now than it used to be.

I once heard it said that we are the sum total of our life's experiences, the people we know, the relationships we have and the books we read. I could have added the words (good or bad) following each of those…."life's experiences, good or bad," "our relationships, good or bad" and so on. That is so true. I've also heard it said a number of times that it is not the good or bad things that happen to us in life that make us who we are but how we handle those things that really determine how we define our lives. That is also so true. Things happen and that's life.

Not too long ago I was having coffee with a good male friend of mine. We've talked on many occasions and he knows me pretty well. He was encouraging me and told me how proud he was of me for all I have gone through and endured in my life. He said "Linda, you should be one pretty messed up woman, but you're not. You are always so upbeat and full of life. Your energy and enthusiasm should be bottled and made available for consumption by others who are too busy complaining about life and how unfair it is." He's right, now. It hasn't always been that way but there came a point when I made the decision that I love life and living. The alternatives really don't interest me.

After an extended period of counseling with my church counselor, he must have agreed. He asked me if I would be willing to share my story and my testimony with the congregation. It would be a healing step and could possibly encourage others in their daily lives. At first I was reluctant. I had never really spoken in public or to more than a small group of people. I didn't know that what I would have to say would be anything of interest to someone else. I was even a little concerned that if people knew about some of the things I went through in my life, they might think less of me. However, I felt I needed to take this next step. It was part of my journey, and part of the healing process. With a great deal of encouragement, reassurance and prayer I agreed and went about putting my story down on paper. Then, the pre-determined Sunday came. Chanel and I arrived at church and, much to my delight, I found I was ready.

After I was introduced by the pastor I looked down at my daughter in the audience and said: "Chanel, are you ready?" This was such a big step for me, to share the story of my life with all my failings in front of so many people. I needed a positive nod from Chanel because she is such an important part of my life and I was about to lay it open for all to see. She gave me that beautiful, innocent smile and nodded her head to say that, "It's okay mom....I love you." So with a deep breath, a heavy sigh and trembling hands, I began to share my story. Here is what I said:

"I've been attending New Hope Church for two years since this last Valentine's Day, in hopes to restore my fourth marriage. The best decision I've ever made was to seek professional marriage counseling and I found a great one through the church. The reason I am sharing this testimony is to extend hope to someone who is listening.

Blessed with Cancer

I have always been a believer in something bigger than myself, just not sure how it all went

together. I thought God and Jesus were the same and that the Holy Spirit fit in there somewhere.

I did not know until two years ago as I attended New Hope and the Cleansing Stream classes

that the Trinity was all there and how they were all related. Wow, to imagine I missed forty

years plus of that.

I grew up in the Mormon religion (LDS church) and was baptized at six years of age. I

believe I had Jesus in my heart before then and I always felt that I was a chosen one. I knew I

was special and that God had a plan for my life. However, as a child I was very confused

growing up to say the least. My mother was a diagnosed paranoid schizophrenic and as a result

of that, I never really knew what was real and what wasn't. To make things worse, I didn't have

the capacity at age thirteen to understand all of that. I didn't realize it at the time but, looking

back, I can see that my father was an alcoholic, which only magnified the situation. Nothing

seemed real, safe or secure for me. Guidance wasn't something I knew about, nor was it part of

my awareness. My dream was to have a family, a functioning mother and father that loved and

protected me and would give me all that I desired in my heart. At age four, my mother and

father divorced, leaving me and my two brothers confused and having to fend pretty much for

ourselves. My younger brother was two and my older brother was eight. I felt more like a child

servant, always being told to" get a diaper, give something to your brothers, walk with your

brother, wait for your brother, like I was somehow responsible for them. I didn't understand it.

I just thought that was the way it was supposed to be and I just did what I was told. As I grew

older I became the surrogate mother to my two brothers and to my alcoholic mother. Who was I

to be thrown into this role? My life was short on role models.

Blessed with Cancer

When I was just thirteen my mother told me to go live with my dad and she helped me out by putting all my clothes on the front porch and telling me to leave. She told me I was never to return to that home again and I never did. The sense of confusion was unbearable. I thought I was going to die. I went to live with my father until I graduated from high school.

There were people in my life who told me how sweet and special I was, including my teachers, the bishop of our church and a few of my friends. But that wasn't what I experienced at home where it really mattered. Even though I heard the encouraging words as they were spoken, they didn't resonate inside. I didn't believe them. I never understood my value as a person....or my value as God intended for me and I didn't have a mentor to tell me differently. Fortunately, although I had good reason, I never turned to drugs or alcohol. Instead, and I can't tell you where it came from, I made the decision that my drug of choice would be to be successful in my career. That is where all my focus, time and energy went. That's all I cared about and that is how I survived. That is what drove me forward. God had to be steering my life, with his angels protecting me, or life would have all turned out differently. He opened the doors that changed my life and helped me be to be successful. One such door was opened following my twenty-fifth birthday and a huge surprise was waiting behind that door.

I was so excited and blessed to be accepted as a flight attendant with Alaska Airlines. What a wonderful opportunity. At the time, it was my dream job. Girls at my age wanted to fly with the airlines and, hopefully see the world. I knew I would be traveling, which means I needed a birth certificate and passport. I had never needed one before so off to the courthouse I went.

While going through the application process I made a rather shocking discovery. There was no record of a Kay Woods. As I made phone calls to family members, secrets were revealed to me for the very first time. I eventually received my birth certificate and learned that the name

Blessed with Cancer

actually listed on the official document was Linda Kay Casto. Linda Kay Casto? Who is that? This was so totally unexpected, I wasn't sure if it was real. The first thought that came to mind was: "Is this really me or some kind of a mistake? If it is not a mistake, then it must be true. If so, then "Who Am I, really?"

What I was to learn is that my mother had divorced my birth father. Even to this date I've never met my biological father. When I was about six months old, my mother married my step-dad. She was worried that he might find out so in order to hide my identity from by birth father, I was raised using my middle name with my new last name, Woods. For twenty-five years I didn't know my real name. The truth was kept from me. When you finally find out the truth, it's numbing. I was stopped cold in my tracks. It took me years to accept that and understand the reason that my mother felt it necessary to hide my real name. I went back to work at the airlines as Linda Casto, but they knew me as Kay Woods. To keep things simpler and not have to explain a lot, I continued to try to hide my real identity.

Since I am being completely honest, I thought I would share with you some of the self-destruction I created, trying to hide and cover up my names:

First, I thought marriage would be the answer. It wasn't. Through four failed marriages, my last name changed from Woods to Peterson to Grill to Kipers and finally, to Mobley. I believed each man would save me and fill the empty gap in my heart. During this time, the greatest blessing of all happened during my second marriage when I was blessed with a beautiful daughter, Chanel. Of all my decisions, good or bad, she was the one that I had planned for. Chanel was a huge gift and an extra special blessing from God. I look back and believe God was telling me He loved me and everything was going to be alright. I now had a reason for hope and a reason to live. This gift would someday save my life.

Blessed with Cancer

Other choices that I made along the way weren't my best. My first husband didn't want to have kids so when I got pregnant I had an abortion, not once but twice. I'm not proud of that now but it is a decision I made at the time. Because of some of my other immature choices, I experienced bankruptcy and financial destruction. I didn't know if I would ever get out from under the effects of these choices. There was a point when my life was spinning out of control. Things were not going well and God wasn't done with the greatest challenge I was yet to face.

This challenge was not a choice or a result of my lifestyle. With everything else going on around me I was diagnosed with breast cancer, stage five, and eventually had to endure the procedures of a double radical mastectomy. Because it was stage five there was very little time to make important decisions. Talk about being out of control and not knowing where to turn. Through the course of six major surgeries, and through the pain and suffering, God spared me. As He gave me back my life, and I was so happy to be alive, I made another mistake and too quickly married my fourth husband. I thought this was another blessing and I was excited about life again. However, I was to learn it would be another test of my resolve to live and love life. During this time I would have to endure domestic violence in the form of psychological abuse, the constant assaults of my husbands' sexual addiction, beyond what I thought possible. I constantly asked myself when it was going to end. Fortunately, during this period in my life my daughter was given freedom from all this pain and insecurity. She had made the decision to move back to live with her birth father and stepmother where she was provided a safe haven. I was grateful for her security and that she would still be living in town, nearby, so I could see her occasionally. But, I didn't want her to experience or see what I was going through. I was now alone and in survival mode.

Blessed with Cancer

At this point my life was spinning out of control. There was only one way I could see to get out from under this abusive life. For me, murder or suicide were not options. By now I had sold my business and gave everything I owned to my new husband. I had no money, moved into a women's shelter and was gleaning food from a local food bank. I was in survival mode. The only thing that was keeping me sane and helping me to get through this was that I could always call on my heavenly Father. In addition, the church I was attending provided a wonderfully caring and compassionate pastoral counselor.

I knew my life wasn't going the way I'd always imagined it. I realized something had to change. I checked myself into an emergency room in order to seek relief and, in a way, escape from life. My reason for checking in was for my mental health. I wanted to mentally check out because I couldn't deal with it anymore. I needed the rest. However, they wouldn't admit me for mental health reasons, even though I believed I was going to snap. I thought I was losing it. I couldn't do it any more. I HAD NOTHING – no job, no car, no money and questionable health. Finally, through this up and down experience, God got my attention and I began to listen. That is when He worked His miracle in my life.

While in the shelter, at my lowest point, I truly prayed out to God to heal me and to give me strength and I finally heard His answer. What I heard was "Let go and let Me." One day as I lay crying at the shelter, God sent an angel. Her name was Tamara Woods. What a coincidence. That was my maiden name. Tamara would place a cup of coffee by my bed every day, along with a burning candle and some scripture from the book of Proverbs. She did that each day before she went off to work. One day those things weren't there. I looked everywhere, but there was no Tamara, no Proverbs and no candle. I realized on that day that if things were going to change I had to go searching on my own, starting with the Proverbs of the Day. My angel had gotten me through my lowest and toughest times but now it was time for me to take responsibility for my actions, or inactions and do whatever it takes to get up and get going again. That realization is what truly saved my life.

Good or bad, consequences do happen. This time they are good. My life was transformed truly by choice. We can choose to be mad, angry, hurt and disappointed or we can choose to see the blessings in our decisions and circumstances. I now have faith stronger than ever before that God loves me, Kay Woods or Linda Mobley, or any combination. With that, I have my family, my friends, and most importantly in this whole world, my daughter back in my life. My wonderful daughter, Chanel, has forgiven me and believes in me again. In advance of Mothers Day, Chanel gave me the best gift I could ever ask for. She told me that she trusts me again and that is the very thing that I wanted most in my life.

Today, God has given me the desires of my heart. All my life I wanted to be a wife, a mother and have a family, a beautiful home, a nice car and money in the bank. I thought I had never left God out of my life. But when I realized there were times when I had, and I was no longer focused on Him, I lost it all. I made the choice to restore my relationship with my Lord and He has restored my relationship with my daughter. In the process, I've also learned the value of forgiveness, first with myself and then with others. That forgiveness has opened up my fellowship with the Lord like I never thought possible. Life couldn't be better for me now that I am God's girl, seated in pew seven, at 11:00 am every Sunday morning. I belong to Him and He's my husband.

Happy Mother's Day to every mother that gave you life and may God richly bless you today. I want to invite my daughter, Chanel, to join me up here. I love her so much and I want to give

Blessed with Cancer

her the gift of these flowers, to thank her for the beauty she brings to my life and for the honor I have in being her mother. Chanel?"

Wow! I was so proud when Chanel smiled at me and joined me up at the front of the sanctuary I couldn't stop hugging her. I was so filled with joy and love that I was no longer aware that I had just spoken in front of over twenty-five hundred people and shared my very personal story. The pastor then stepped up to me and Chanel. As he put his arms around both of us he asked the congregation to lift up their hands to God for me and Chanel and then he prayed a wonderful prayer to God on our behalf. God is so good and his grace endures forever. At that moment the warmth and love of God and all these wonderful friends in the church was an overwhelming affirmation that I was going to be okay. God still has a plan for my life and hasn't given up on Linda Mobley, or Kay Woods, or whatever my name is. What I do know for sure is that I am His child and that He will be with me always. That's His promise.

Chapter 12 – Faith, Prayer and the Broken Glass

*"I know God will not give me anything I can't handle.
I just wish He didn't trust me so much."* Mother Theresa

I can't believe I have reached the last chapter already. I've almost finished telling my story and this is probably going to be the shortest chapter of my book. However, don't think it is the whole story. There is so much more I'd like to share with you and, if I get the chance to meet with you at some future time, I'll tell you more. Besides, this isn't the end. It is just the beginning of the rest of my life, a life I am so grateful to have.

Since even before learning that I had cancer, my life was an adventure with all kinds of twists and turns, ups and downs, wins and losses, successes and failures, all lived with the unintended purpose of preparing me for my most recent and unexpected adventure. Since that day of discovering the cancer within me, my life was changed and I could no longer take for granted all that life has to offer. I was instilled with a new challenge, the greatest and most potentially devastating of my life. Some would call it a crossroad. My friend in the movie industry would call it a paradigm shift, where a new unknown element of the story would be revealed and create a new understanding. This would take the plot in a whole new direction.

Discovering the lump and learning that it was cancer was a paradigm shift for my life. Things were no longer as they had been and could no longer be as they were. I had to make a decision, to either shrivel up in fear or fight with every ounce within me. That meant all my strength and will, with the committed discipline to, in the words of Winston Churchill, "Never Give Up." That little quotation from a long-forgotten world history lesson was never made more relevant in my life than at that moment. I couldn't give up. I had to live for Chanel.

Blessed with Cancer

As I thought about how to relate the pain of my life in hopes of encouraging you in yours, I'm reminded of a very old movie a friend once told me about. He didn't remember the title because it was so long ago but thought it may have been an Alfred Hitchcock film because he remembers it was in the style of Hitchcock. It kept him on the edge of his seat. He remembered one scene that he felt really symbolized the unexpected pains we experience in our lives. The gist of the story is this:

The female lead was a blind woman who lived alone in a big house and tried to tell people there was a man stalking her. No one believed her. In the climactic, final segment of the film the man broke into her home and she became aware of his presence when she heard him knock some glasses off the kitchen counter, causing them to shatter all over the floor. As she tried to elude her would-be killer and escape the house she was forced to exit through the kitchen. Unfortunately, she had removed her shoes in order to walk quietly without the killer hearing her. As she went through the kitchen, trying to escape, she kept stepping on the multiple shards of glass that covered the floor, cutting through her tender feet and causing excruciating pain as well as leaving a trail of blood for her pursuer to follow. The pain was horrendous and strung out through the lengthy chase to the final conclusion and eventual rescue.

The broken glass symbolizes for me what it felt like so many times in my life with my failed relationships, painful back surgery, getting the boys, losing the boys, selling my business, becoming a single mom again and, eventually, all the pain I experienced while fighting to survive my cancer. I felt as though no matter where I stepped, my tender, bare feet found the broken glass as it cut into my life in so many painful ways. Where can you go or where can you step without feeling the pain of the broken glass? Just like in the movie, in order to survive the

Blessed with Cancer

killer I had to bear up under the pain, ignore what was being done to my life and keep moving

forward until I could reach safety.

Thus began the latest adventure for Linda Mobley. It was a long, torturous trip that would

test me to the very limits of my being. I could not have done it without two very important

beliefs I possess and hold so dear. Without them I don't know how I could have survived this

experience. Those two beliefs, solid pillars that held me up, are faith and prayer and, together,

they helped me make it through this journey. They were as important to my life as are breathing,

eating and loving and they are just as important today.

Prayer was a constant for me during this long and difficult time dealing with my cancer and

the recovery. Not only did I pray many times throughout the day, I know that I had many

friends, customers and associates who were also praying on my behalf. It was always such a

comfort to me, just to know that so many people cared and were lifting me up in prayer to the

Great Physician. I know him as God. Others prefer to call Him the Great Healer or the

Benevolent One. Regardless of whether you believe in the healing power of the Almighty or

whether you even believe that there is a God at all, I certainly believe. I couldn't have gotten

through this without knowing that a Higher Power was watching over me. Over the years, as He

promised, God continues to prove His faithfulness and I've experienced that promise many times

in my life.

Think about this for a moment. If you don't believe in God and there really is no God, what

is the harm of someone praying for you or you praying for yourself? The answer is simple.

There is no harm. You have nothing to lose. However, if you don't believe in God and, in fact,

there really is a God but no one is praying for you, including you, what have you lost? The

answer may be "everything." So what have you got to lose? I hope you do believe there is a

Blessed with Cancer

God, a Benevolent One, a Higher Power. Even if you don't, go ahead and ask a believer if they would pray for you. You must know someone that will pray for you and who would ask their believer friends to pray for you, as well. It couldn't hurt, yet it may make all the difference in the world. By the way, if you are a believer you'll probably be praying yourself, as well as asking your family and friends to also pray. It's such a simple thing to do and it's free.

On the subject of prayer, if you still don't see any value in it here is a scientific endorsement for prayer. It is a known fact that people who are prayed for do much better in surgery and in their personal recovery than those who are not prayed for. I read recently that there have been studies done to find out if this is true. In this study quite a few patients, unbeknownst to them, were either placed in a group that was prayed for or in another group that was not prayed for. During their medical procedures and recovery period, there were volunteers who had agreed to be part of the study and pray for specific patients. I am assuming these individuals are believers and they pray for the patients that are on the "pray for" list. For whatever reason, and there is no direct scientific explanation other than the results of the study, those who were prayed for had much higher degrees of success in their procedures and recovery outcomes. During the study the participating hospitals, as well as the doctors, nurses and technicians, were the same staff for both groups of patients. The only variable in the study was that someone was praying for one of the two groups of patients. Therefore, the study would lead one to the conclusion that there is power in prayer.

You can believe or you can choose not to believe, but those patients who received prayer actually did better all around and had a better survival rate with a better physical healing outcome. That is good enough for me. People were praying for me and my procedures and outcome went very well. I survived and I'm cancer-free today. I was already a believer so it

Blessed with Cancer

was very easy for me to want my friends and family to pray for me. I am also grateful that so many people, even those I didn't know, were praying for me. I later learned that customers, neighbors and other business people in my community were also praying for me. The love, support and prayers I received were over-whelming and I was so grateful.

The other pillar that helped hold me up and get me through the most difficult times was Faith. Webster's New World College Dictionary defines faith as *"unquestioning belief that does not require proof or evidence."* It is *"complete trust, confidence or reliance."* Based on this definition we all have faith on a daily basis to some degree, in most of the simple things like sitting in a chair, starting the car and driving somewhere or even crossing a bridge. Maybe those examples aren't the purest forms of faith but they do require trust that the chair, the car or the bridge were built correctly, with all the safeguards required and they will not collapse under us. I think we can also all agree that it takes a level of faith or trust; however you choose to identify it, to board an airplane to fly somewhere. You believe and have faith that the plane was constructed properly, inspected regularly, maintained correctly and that the flight crew is qualified and has met their annual physical and flight certifications as required. That's a lot to think about and, for the most part, we probably don't want to think that deeply about it. We just want to fly somewhere.

For the greater issues in life and especially for the ones we have absolutely no control over, I prefer to rely on the way the Bible defines FAITH in Hebrews 11:1. ***"Faith is the substance of things hoped for, the evidence of things not seen."*** Your faith allows you to know it in your heart and mind and that gives you the peace and comfort you need to move forward.

When I discovered the lump in my breast and it was confirmed that I had cancer, I didn't turn to Webster for a definition. I was scared to death and I needed the assurance that I was going to

Blessed with Cancer

be okay. I hoped and prayed and hoped and prayed some more that I would be alright, that I would realize "*the evidence of things not seen.*" I couldn't see into the future and know what the outcome would be. But, I did know what my first steps would be and that was to pray and then have faith that God had heard my prayer.

I've also learned through this horrifying experience that you can't really rely on either prayer or faith alone. You need both. I certainly did. I'm reminded of an old chorus sung in church that provides a visual confirmation of the relevance of prayer to faith. It goes like this:

"Prayer is the key to heaven, but faith unlocks the door.

Words are so easily spoken, but prayer without faith,

Is like a boat without an oar,

Have faith when you speak to the Master, that's all He asks you for.

Yes, prayer is the key to heaven, but faith unlocks the door."

Faith and prayer gave me what I needed to make it through my experience.

There is one more necessary step. After you have engaged prayer and faith, or whatever means you use to accept and wrap around your challenge, you can't stop there. Now you need to take ACTION. Don't wait. As the NIKE slogan says, "JUST DO IT!" Whatever next step you need to do, do it now! Don't put it off. Time is not on your side. When I discovered the lump in my breast and I suspected it might be cancer but wasn't sure, I didn't wait to see if it would go away. I called my doctor and set up an appointment to see him right away. I wanted to know. I needed to know. I've already seen the heartache and pain caused by this deadly disease and too many women, and some men, didn't take it serious enough until it was too late.

If you're not sure what to do call someone, whether it's a family member, a trusted friend or a professional. Do something now. Take action. Get to your doctor as soon as possible. Don't be

Blessed with Cancer

embarrassed that it may be a false alarm. If it is, be grateful. If it is not, be thankful that you took action and it was found earlier than if you had waited. I can't emphasize this enough. Take action! Your life may depend on it. Faith is good but faith without action is foolish. C.S. Lewis confirms the need to have faith and action when he was once asked which is more important. His response says it best. "Asking which is more important, faith or actions, is like asking which blade in a pair of scissors is more necessary." Okay, did I mention you need both faith and action?

As a final thought, I want to share something with you that was recently sent to me in an e-mail by a good friend. I was so touched by the reminder and the relevance it has in my life, especially during my recovery years, that I thought it could be an encouragement to you as well. I just wish I knew to whom the credit should go. I was already familiar with the message because I'd read the original presentation in the Bible (Ecclesiastes 3:1-8) but it served to remind me that everything happens for a reason. Back in the early 1960s it was also put to music in a very popular song presented by a singing group called The Byrds. Some of you may remember when it was so popular. I have to admit, it was just around the time I was born and I'm sure I don't recall hearing it at that time. However, I've heard it many times since and was reminded again of its message when I received the e-mail. It was entitled The Seasons of People In Your Life. I want to share it with you.

"People come into your life for a REASON, a SEASON or a LIFETIME. When you know which one it is, you will know what to do for that person. When someone is in your life for a REASON, it is usually to meet a need you have expressed. They have come to assist you through a difficulty, to provide you with guidance and support, to aid you physically, emotionally or spiritually. They may seem like a godsend, and they are. They are there for a reason you need

them to be. Then, without any wrongdoing on your part or at an inconvenient time, this person will say or do something to bring the relationship to an end. Sometimes they die. Sometimes they walk away. Sometimes they act up and force you to take a stand. What we must realize is that our need has been met, our desire fulfilled, their work is done. The prayer you sent up has been answered and now it is time to move on."

"Some people come into your life for a SEASON because your turn has come to share, grow or learn. They bring you an experience of peace or make you laugh. They may teach you something you have never done. They usually give you an unbelievable amount of joy. Believe it, it is real, but, only for a season."

"LIFETIME relationships teach you lifetime lessons, things you must build upon in order to have a solid emotional foundation. Your job is to accept the lesson, love the person and put what you have learned into use in all other relationships and areas of your life. It is said that love is blind, but friendship is clairvoyant." Author unknown.

When you think about it, this is one of those gifts of life. When I read it I was reminded of all the people that came in and out of my life during my bout with cancer, and even since. Some are still friends today and others have moved on. I am eternally grateful for all those people and for the roles they played to impact my life in some way. I will never forget them. With the new and expanding opportunities I have to share my story I continue to meet people and develop new friendships.

Your life is also a gift. It is a gift to you and all those with whom you come in contact. You are special. You are unique and "one of a kind," among all mankind. Even twins are unique in their own way. No two individuals are completely alike. Every life and every soul is precious. Every breath breathed confirms you are alive and you can make a difference. The only constant

Blessed with Cancer

in our lives is time. Like every other human being you have sixty seconds in a minute and sixty minutes in an hour. You have twenty-four hours in a day and seven days in a week. What you don't know is how many minutes, days or weeks you have left in your life. How you spend that time is critical to the impact you will have on this earth. You will either utilize the time to its fullest or you will waste it or do something in between. You will apply yourself to making the world better for those around you or you won't. If you focus on what is possible and apply yourself there you will achieve so much more than those who focus on what can't be done. The choice is yours. Please choose wisely.

For all of you that have touched my life in some way, thank you for being there. For all those I've yet to meet, I look forward to that time. You are an important part of the whole of my existence and I count you among all the many blessings I've received and those yet to come. Thank you! May your life be as full of such gifts and may you see them for the blessings they are in YOUR life.

Epilogue

A Letter to My New Friends

"Discover, develop and apply your talents, for those are gifts to be used in service to others." Dr. Eric Allenbaugh

My dear friend,

Thank you for reading my story and sharing in my life this way. You are a very special person and I am grateful to you, even though I may have never met you. This has been an interesting journey for me in a number of ways. Through the process of writing this book, I have had to dig up, and in some cases dig very deeply, many of the memories that I'd suppressed for a long time. Recounting those experiences caused me to run through the full range of emotions, many of which were very painful at the time. I had to experience that pain again, at least in my mind. Writing this book has also been a surprisingly healing process for me. Putting it down on paper, speaking it out loud and sharing it with so many people has helped me to experience some level of closure to that part of my life. The personal acknowledgement that I had breast cancer, went through all the pain, doubt and accompanying fear and survived it all has prepared me to move forward in my life and is preparing me for my next great adventure. It also proves that God is not done with me yet. There is more to come.

I felt that if I could touch just one person or encourage another suffering soul by sharing my story, I did what I had intended to do with the writing of this book. As you know, life is not always easy and, for some, it is downright difficult. However, and you've probably heard it before, I have learned that it is not the challenges in life that determines the quality of life, it is how we respond to those challenges and what we do with them. We have that free will to choose.

Blessed with Cancer

Ask yourself how you are handling the challenges in your life. You can be angry and blame everyone and everything around you or you can accept your circumstances and decide that you will control your own destiny. This way of thinking can change your life or the life of someone close to you, starting today. I, too, had a choice and I chose to count my blessings and fight.

As you've read this story, please keep in mind that it is just one story, my story. It is the story as I lived it and recalled it. Still, there are so many other stories out there and each is unique to the woman, or the man, who has had to fight his/her own battles and shape his/her own stories. Some survived and some didn't. Some may even still be fighting. If you know of such a person, whoever they are, you can help them through it with your unconditional love, your caring heart, your deep compassion and your earnest understanding, although you may not totally understand what they are going through. When you give to them, with no expectation of anything in return, you will be blessed beyond measure, guaranteed.

Just one final thought. My wish for you is that you have the very best life possible, regardless of your circumstances. Mark Twain once said it like this about life: "Dance like no one is watching. Sing like no one is listening. Love like you've never been hurt, and live like it's Heaven on Earth." That's great advice. You have the rest of your life with the opportunity to choose to live it any way you want, including choosing to live life to the fullest. Give it all you've got. Live it every day as though it is your last and touch others along the way. You will be blessed and their lives will be enriched beyond what you ever thought possible, whether you know it at the time or not. God bless you.

With much love,

Acknowledgements

No story gets put on paper and comes to life in book without the support and encouragement of so many people, some providing valuable input and others providing their moral support. I want to thank everyone who, along the way, could see the growth that has occurred and the potential for telling a story that would hopefully help so many other people. When you start acknowledging those people, there isn't room to acknowledge everyone and, you run the risk of overlooking someone whose encouragement has been critical to the success and completion. So, I will do my best to acknowledge a select group of friends, but my love and gratitude goes out to everyone who has made this possible.

First I want to thank my beautiful daughter Chanel who lived this story with me from the beginning and has always been my biggest supporter and fan. I want to thank my good friend Charles Waugh of Charles Waugh Fine Art Portraits for the beautiful photos on the book cover, and for his encouragement from the very beginning. Marinella Jiganie is one of my newest friends who came alongside to help create the beautiful book cover design and continues to bring her gifted talents to promote the <u>Blessed With Cancer</u> vision. T.J. Hoisington, himself a nationally recognize author and motivational speaker, has provided guidance and encouragement to help me see this through. Not to be left out, I want to thank another good friend Ron Gladney, who steered me toward and helped me understand the world of social media and its "role" of getting the word out to the world.

I want to share a special thank you to my forever beautiful friend, Katie Harman Ebner for so graciously writing the forward to my book and for being a champion to spur me on to share my story. There is also my best friend and brother-in-Christ, Lee Robinson Jr., who counseled and pushed me with grace and love to finish the race and never give up. I need to express my great

Blessed with Cancer

appreciation to a new friend, Barbara Blix, whose masterful editing skills not only prepared the final manuscript for printing, but taught us so much in the process.

I also want to thank the wonderful friends, authors and leaders who took the time to review the manuscript and graciously provided their generous endorsements as listed on the cover as well as inside the book. Their expressed support for the book is a huge encouragement for what this story has to offer and I will forever be grateful. I am especially thankful to Chuck Whitlock, a master of providing leadership through the written word, who generously provided his experience and guidance in the process of bringing this book to market.

And finally, I want to express my deepest appreciation and love for my writer, manager and close friend Ron Carr, whose patience, sensitivity and creative skills made it possible to bring my experience to life in such a dynamic and profound way. Through my tears, confusion, struggles and musings, Ron took the smorgasbord of stories, words and emotions and brought focus and cohesiveness to help me share this challenging and blessed chapter in my life in such a clear and poignant way.

If I have missed anyone, please forgive me and know how much I love you and I am grateful for the touch of your life on my journey. Thank you and may God richly bless you.

Speaker Information

If you would like to invite Linda Mobley to be a speaker for your organization, association or special event, please contact us at:

info@blessedwithcancerthebook.com

Or, write to us at

Blessed With Cancer
P.O. Box 87151
Vancouver, WA 98687

Or call us at:
360-358-0622

Book Orders

Books are available for order online at our website

www.blessedwithcancerthebook.com

Quantity discounts are also available for orders of 12 books or more.

NOTES

MORE NOTES

LOTS OF NOTES